Clarinet Exam Pack

ABRSM Grade 2

Selected from the 2018–2021 syllabus

Name

Date of exam

C000063637

Contents

Consultant Editor for ABRSM: David Blackwell
Footnotes: Dominic Wells

Other pieces for Grade 2

LIST A

LIST B

LIST C

First published in 2017 by ABRSM (Publishing) Ltd,
a wholly owned subsidiary of ABRSM, 4 London Wall Place,
London EC2Y 5AU, United Kingdom
© 2017 by The Associated Board of the Royal Schools of Music
Distributed worldwide by Oxford University Press

Music origination by Julia Bovee and Katie Johnston (Sight-reading)
Cover by Kate Benjamin & Andy Potts
Printed in England by Page Bros (Norwich) Ltd,
on materials from sustainable sources.
Reprinted in 2019

A:1

Allegro

K. 3

Arranged by David Blackwell

W. A. Mozart
(1756–91)

This little Allegro was written for piano on 4th March 1762, and from the 'K.' (Köchel) catalogue number, we know that this is one of Mozart's earliest works – in fact, he was just six years old when he wrote it!

This arrangement by David Blackwell features the lowest or 'chalumeau' register of the clarinet. The elegant, legato phrasing (e.g. the pairs of quavers in bars 5–6) contrasts with the cheeky staccato notes (e.g. bar 7). Another feature is the many dynamic markings: sometimes these are sudden, such as the *p* in bar 8 following an *mf* passage; at other times they are more gradual (through a *crescendo*).

The Trout

Arranged by Nancy Litten

Franz Schubert
(1797–1828)

Although Schubert died when he was just 31 years old, he managed to compose over 600 Lieder (German songs) in his brief lifetime. *Die Forelle* ('The Trout') is one of the most-loved and famous of all his songs – so famous in fact, that Schubert was commissioned to re-use the melody in a Piano Quintet, which became one of his most celebrated chamber pieces. This arrangement was inspired by both of these works.

The song tells the story of a person watching a trout swimming in a stream, before a fisherman catches it. Its light-hearted, humorous character is expressed through the phrasing – in particular the staccato notes and slurs – leading to a singing-like quality.

I Love My Love

Arranged by Alan Bullard

Trad. Cornish

I Love My Love is a folk song from Cornwall, a picturesque county on the south-west tip of England. The Cornish cliffs look out to sea, and unsurprisingly the words of this song include seafaring images. It tells of a boy and a girl in love. One day the boy's parents send him off to sea, but eventually his boat returns and he is reunited with his beloved. Despite this happy ending, the piece has a mournful, longing quality, best served by legato playing, and shaping each phrase as if you were telling someone a story.

The song is perhaps more widely known today in an arrangement for choir by Gustav Holst: the composer of *The Planets*.

Oom-Pah-Pah

from Oliver!

B:1

Arranged by David Blackwell

Lionel Bart
(1930–99)

Taken from the popular musical, *Oliver!* (based on Charles Dickens's novel *Oliver Twist*), the song 'Oom-Pah-Pah' is sung by Nancy, a market-seller. She is one of the few characters who looks out for Oliver, a poor orphan who has become involved with a young gang of thieves. Nancy sings this song to distract the others, so that Oliver can escape to a better life with Mr Brownlow, a kind gentleman who adopts him.

In the musical, the setting for this song is a pub. At the start you play Nancy singing the verse, and when you reach the chorus (bar 21) imagine a lively crowd singing and swinging along with you!

B:2

Definitely!

No. 2 from *November Blues*

Mike Cornick
(born 1947)

The subtitle of this piece – No. 2 from *November Blues* – offers a clue about its character. The Blues is a type of jazz, and every bar shows the influence of this musical style, in particular the blue notes (notes flattened by a semitone) and swung quavers. A good sense of rhythm and especially pulse is important in this piece: notice how some of the phrases start on the beat, while others begin off the beat.

Mike Cornick studied composition at Trinity College of Music and is now best known for his jazz piano publications.

Getting to the Front of the Queue

 B:3

Paul Harris

Being patient isn't always easy, especially when you have to wait in a queue – at the dentist; the cinema; the supermarket. That's what this piece is all about, so when playing it, take your time – don't rush, and don't skip ahead in the queue! The dynamic range might represent your mood along the way: perhaps the louder passage at bar 9 suggests becoming a little impatient, before calming down again a few bars later.

Paul Harris studied the clarinet at the Royal Academy of Music and is one of the UK's leading music educationalists, with over six hundred publications to his name.

C:1

Tenuto Study No. 9 in G

from 'Die einfachsten Vortragsarten' from *Elementarschule für Klarinette*

Friedrich Demnitz
(1845–90)

Friedrich Demnitz was a virtuoso clarinettist of the late 19th century. He is known by clarinet students all over the world for his *Elementarschule für Klarinette* (*Elementary School for Clarinet*) – a collection of studies focusing on different techniques of the instrument.

This particular study from 'Die einfachsten Vortragsarten' ('The simplest forms of phrasing') section aims to improve your tenuto playing. 'Tenuto' originates from the Latin word 'tenere', which means 'to hold'. Although not marked by tenuto marks (♩), all notes should be held for their full duration.

Castle Waltz

No. 8 from *21st-Century Clarinet Studies*

 C:2

Colin Radford
(born 1959)

Before you start playing this piece, try to picture a castle in your mind. There's an old, grand ballroom, but it's not full of people; just two figures, dancing a waltz together. There's a slightly spooky feel to this dance. It's quiet, and the phrases are short, as if the dancers are pausing at the final crotchet of each phrase. At bar 9 the melody (now in a major key) is raised an octave higher. Here, the dancers relax a little, with a slightly louder dynamic and longer phrases, before returning to the more formal style of the opening. A *ritardando* draws the waltz to a graceful conclusion.

Colin Radford has performed as a clarinet soloist for the BBC and international radio and television, as well as having played with several London orchestras.

C:3

Continental Breakfast

James Rae
(born 1957)

People often refer to a 'Continental breakfast' to distinguish it from an 'English breakfast'. Instead of sausages, eggs and bacon, you'd have toast, cereals and pastries. Articulation and dynamics really help bring out the character of this piece. Perhaps the tentative staccato notes at the beginning suggest tiptoeing downstairs without waking anyone up. At bar 5 you see all the food before you on the table, and by bar 9 you're gulping down your cereal. Four bars later (the *f*), toast is popping up and you're reaching out for the butter and jam. You've just room for one final mouthful, before tiptoeing away and gently closing the door behind you.

Having studied clarinet, bass clarinet, piano and composition at the Guildhall School of Music and Drama, James Rae has pursued a successful and varied career in music.

© 2017 by The Associated Board of the Royal Schools of Music

Scales and arpeggios

SCALES

from memory
tongued *and* slurred

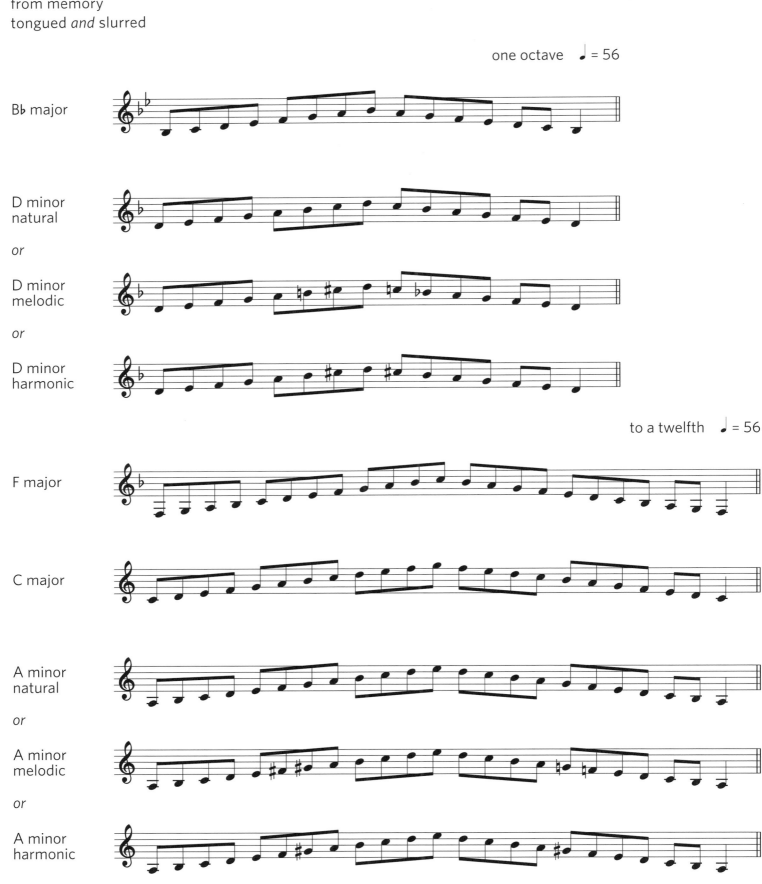

ARPEGGIOS

from memory
tongued *and* slurred

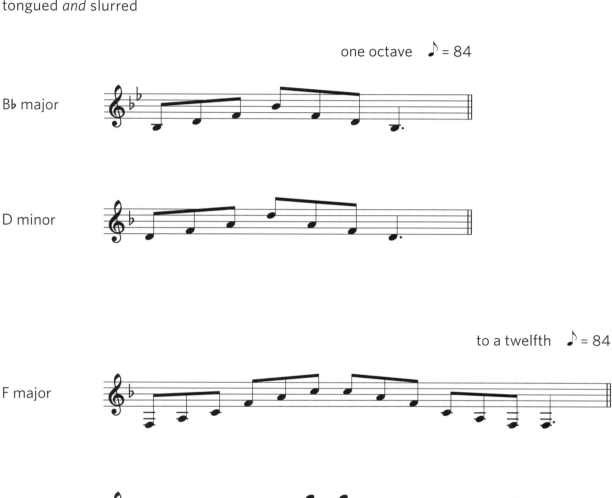

14

Sight-reading

Sight-reading

Sight-reading

HIT PARADE

HEROES

Editor: MIKE EVANS

Design: SUE MICHNIEWICZ

Production Controller: MICHELLE THOMAS

Picture Research: CLAIRE TAYLOR

Acknowledgements:
Aquarius:- 31, 47, 87, 94b, 115, 117, 127, 128, 130, 143, 144 inset, 146b, 148r, 153, 155, 156b, 157b. BBC Photograph Library:- 13b, 104. Big H. Productions:- 5, 35r. Mary Evans Picture Library:- Roger Mayne: 6, 9, 38, 43t, 49l, 84. Ronald Grant Archives:- 12, 15, 18b, 24, 29b, 37, 48t, 56b, 57 88, 89l, 89r,90l, 91l, 91r, 92, 93, 97, 99, 100t, 100b, 102b, 108, 116, 121, 131, 133, 134, 137, 138, 141. Hulton-Deutsch Collection:- back cover, 7t, 10, 42, 76r, 118-119. London Features International:- all pictures on front cover, 21, 28, 32t, 40, 41t, 59, 63, 65, 96l, 103, 106, 114, 125, 132, 136, 139, 144, 145, 151, 156t, 157t; Michael Ochs Collection: 60. Paramount:- 53r. Pictorial Press:- 44t, 52t, 53l, 122. Popperfoto:- 10, 16b, 17, 20-21, 22, 29t, 30, 32b, 34t, 35l, 46, 48b, 50, 56t, 58, 61, 66, 66-67, 75r, 76l, 81, 101, 107l, 120, 129, 135, 142, 149, 150, 154. Rank:- 92-93. Redferns:- Glenn A. Baker Archives: 90r; Gems: 146t, 152; William Gottlieb: 19; Richie Howells: 27, 109l, 136-137; Bob Vincent: 36; David Redfern: 85, 86, 86-87; Rick Richards: 45b, 74, 108-109, 148l; Robert Smith: 112-113; Robert Vincett: 96-97, 105, 126, 147. Rex:- 41b. Topham Picture Source:- 7b, 11, 14t, 14b, 26, 34b, 43r, 44b, 45t, 49t, 51, 52r, 62, 64, 75l, 77, 78-79, 78l, 78r, 79, 82-83, 83. V & A Museum:- Harry Hammond Collection: 13t, 16t, 20, 23, 33b, 39, 55, 68, 69, 70, 71, 73, 80, 82, 94t, 98, 102t, 107r, 109r, 110l, 110r, 111, 112, 113, 123, 124, 140. Reproduced by permission of Warner Chappell Music Ltd/International Music Publications: 18t, 25, 33t, 54, 67, 95, 118t, 118b, 119.

First published in 1993 by
Hamlyn, an imprint of
Reed Consumer Books Limited,
Michelin House, 81 Fulham Road,
London SW3 6RB
and Auckland, Melbourne, Singapore and Toronto

A Catalogue record for this book is available from the British Library
ISBN 0 600 57899 2

Produced by Mandarin Offset
Printed and bound in Hong Kong

HIT PARADE

HEROES

BRITISH ★ BEAT
Before THE BEATLES

Dave McAleer

HAMLYN

Contents

Most of the significant musical advances in the last hundred years have emanated from America, so I guess it was quite natural that during the fifties the majority of the artistes in Great Britain invariably looked and listened, open-mouthed, to their cousins across the big pond and, to a certain extent, this American creative dominance still persists to this day. Unlike today, however, the biggest single problem that we British artistes faced in those early pop years was quite simply the shortage of world markets due to the natural isolation of this island.

In addition, and no less significantly, the lack of artistic influences showed, without doubt, that being close to the source of inspiration had enormous advantages. Not for us, the sultry Blues voice and guitar playing on the corner of Beale Street, or the fervour of the Gospel Choir in Harlem. Not at all. Most weekends us 'Brits' would be bombarded by the Billy Cotton Band Show shouting through the radios "Wakey Wakey", or serenading us with their rendition of "Where Will The Baby's Dimple Be?", whilst Sunday evenings meant a Palm Court Hotel broadcast, all of which, without doubt, presented myself and my contemporaries with a few inborn musical hurdles to overcome.

In fact, it was these restrictions and the lack of a modern communications network that meant that most of the names in this book never really had the chance to air their talents to the world – unlike our modern compatriots who are able to compete on equal terms.

Despite this, however, Great Britain can be proud of its creative achievements. Without the earlier efforts of the artistes who plied their trade throughout the period covered by this book, the successes that eventually came in the sixties to British artistes such as the Beatles could never have been achieved. Make no mistake, many of the names contained in these pages were and are world-beaters and it was my great privilege to have worked with nearly all of them at one time or another. This was the most exciting period that I personally believe the world has ever experienced, and I feel honoured to have been able to play a small part in it.

On reflection, I think there has been a need for a book like this for a long time and it will provide, I'm sure, a useful reference to everybody with an interest in the history of Pop music.

MARTY WILDE

Introduction

There's no way that the little island of Britain can claim to have invented rock'n'roll or even to have contributed to its birth. The music was born in the USA, and it was America that gave the world all rock's major players in its formative years. However, it should be remembered that there was no shortage of top class rock artists in the UK before The Beatles, and that several superb singles were recorded in Britain between 1956-62. The main purpose of this book is to give (sometimes long overdue) credit to the UK's first rock'n'rollers; while at the same time attempting to put their work into some kind of true perspective.

When it came to selecting 'beat' artists to include, I have erred on the generous side, and included several singers who would not merit inclusion in a strict Who's Who Of Rock. I have also made a conscious effort to go into more depth on the lesser known performers of the era, since many major performers are already well documented. It has also been my aim to avoid the more obvious facts about the top acts, trying instead to include lesser known items that relate to the period covered in the book.

You didn't just go to a record shop to buy a record in the Fifties – you would browse there for hours, socialise, and probably listen to dozens of discs before parting with the price of one

The book includes a glance at the transatlantic pop scene before rock's arrival, and looks in depth at all the important beat-influenced British male and female singers, groups and instrumentalists in those years before the Beatles turned the UK music scene upside down. There are also features on the skiffle and trad jazz crazes that swept the UK, as well as the 'back-room boys' of British rock. Sections on UK rock films, TV and radio programmes and the music press are included, plus chapters about the fashions, dance crazes and the youth culture of the era. The book also examines the American music scene before the Beatles-led British Invasion, and ends with reference to UK pop music as it was represented during the early days of the Beatles.

As can be imagined, after 25 years in the music business I have met many successful and unsuccessful recording artists, producers and back room boys, and realise that every record, whether a hit or miss, has an interesting story behind it. Talking to such people helped fit together many of the pieces that make up the pre-Beatles British music jigsaw. It was my intention to try not to look at topics solely from a record business point of view, although occasionally I may have, and in those cases I hope to have provided an interesting insight. It was initially planned to include many recent remarks from the subjects of *Hit Parade Heroes*, but it soon became apparent that there's 'no quote like an old quote', as hindsight tends a dull the edges of truth, and an artist's words at the time generally give a much better and truer picture of events.

In a nutshell, the ingredients for the rock'n'roll revolution (or is that evolution?) were already in the musical mixing bowl at the dawn of the 1950s. The music exploded in Britain shortly after it had taken America by storm, and, despite considerable opposition from parents, politicians and preachers, it was dominating the UK pop charts by 1957, with Britain's pop protégés scoring alongside their American masters. Although the UK broadcasting media was very slow to give the music the exposure it deserved, rock'n'roll quickly thrived and prospered, and, like most things in life, it evolved, merging with other forms of popular music; sometimes making it impossible to tell where one form stopped and the next one started.

It was a time of a real boom in disc sales, and record shops went all out to serve their increasingly youthful customers with the very latest in audio technology

No doubt some readers will find it difficult to imagine Britain in this bygone era. From a musical point of view, it was a land with little or no pop on the radio or TV and, for the record, in the mid-1950s every single was a breakable 78 rpm 10" platter, many of which were still played on wind-up gramophones (record players).

The Boswell Sisters reached the US Top Ten in 1934 with a song entitled 'Rock And Roll'!

TOP HITS

TOMMY STEELE

LONNIE DONEGAN

CLIFF RICHARD

MARTY WILDE

BILLY FURY

HELEN SHAPIRO

ADAM FAITH

The average wind would last about three singles, at which stage the record would audibly slow down and a vigorous rewind would be called for. The best received technological breakthrough in the record industry during the early 1950s had been the introduction of gramophone needles (a prehistoric stylus) that could play up to ten records before needing replacement. This was a vast improvement on previous needles which were purchased in a box of 100 and which needed changing after every record! The public were far less interested in EMI's announcement that they would be releasing 45 RPM singles on 7" plastic, or that EMI were going to be following Decca's lead and manufacturing 33 ⅓rd RPM long-playing microgroove albums. In fact, the 45 rpm 7" single did not really start catching on in Britain until 1958, and only a few rock'n'roll performers released albums before the early 1960s.

It may help to visualise the record situation in the UK if it is kept in mind that only a handful of companies existed and that the big four – EMI, Decca, Philips and Pye – had the lion's share of all record sales, and therefore controlled the market. There were no notable independent labels and only a couple of independent production companies who leased their product to the majors. Several different record charts existed, but the one most record buyers consulted was the *NME* Top 30, which is referred to throughout this book.

Artist and Repertoire (A&R) men at these companies either produced or selected all the records released. Even in the early 1960s most of these A&R men were from the pre-rock school, which naturally meant that they did not understand the music in the same way as most young record buyers. This situation changed slowly as the sixties progressed, but for the era that this book covers, it is true to say that the majority of music industry people making the decisions about rock 'n'roll (and for that matter most people involved in the record business) in Britain were not genuine rock fans, and hurried home after work to listen to some 'quality music', from the likes of Frank Sinatra, Ella Fitzgerald, Peggy Lee and Nat 'King' Cole.

This would seem a good moment to mention that many of the people actively involved in the making of rock records, and indeed a large number of the fans, had a sneaking suspicion that the bubble would soon burst. Therefore, with the aim of lengthening their careers, several soloists and groups, who had initially hit with rock oriented-releases, quickly attempted to widen their musical parameters and to become 'all-round entertainers'. They wanted to be ready for the night club and cabaret circuit when rock receded; the prospect of returning to the coffee bars and cellar club circuit did not appeal to most of them.

Early British rockers are, of course, not the only ones to get short-changed in most rock books; countless lesser known American artists too seldom receive the credit they deserve in helping sculpt early rock. In the hope of slightly redressing the balance, hundreds of US performers have been name checked who recorded the original versions of songs cut by British acts, information which it is hoped will be of interest. In reality, such a large percentage of the early domestic rock'n'roll recordings were cover versions that the impression may be given that many UK rock'n'rollers were parasites. It is true that if genuine originality is the vital ingredient most of the UK performers of the period don't stand close scrutiny - however, neither do many of the British stars of the Beat Boom era, nor indeed hundreds of other UK or American artists. If all the truly original rock artists squeezed into a five-seater car, there would probably still be room for Elvis, Cliff, Bill Haley and The Everly Brothers.

There's no point in denying that some of the first British rock acts were exploring a musical terrain already well trodden by American artists, but the fact is that several of the UK artists of the era were genuinely creative, and would almost certainly have been successful in the States had they arrived on the scene after The Beatles broke down the door that for so long had kept the

Bill Haley was older than Johnnie Ray, Guy Mitchell and Eddie Fisher, the three major pop stars before the arrival of rock'n'roll

Rock'n'roller skating – the roller rink was a typical social meeting place in the late Fifties

British out. Until The Beatles bulldozed those barriers, UK-produced rock records were regarded very much as second rate in the USA. This reaction understandably appeared to give most UK artists inferiority complexes about the American market. When his US label, Epic, asked Marty Wilde to cut some tracks for the US (after the success there of 'Bad Boy' in 1960), Marty commented, 'I really couldn't believe they would want me to record in America'. Even in 1962, the year that The Beatles first charted in the UK, top British vocalist Eden Kane stated (after returning from a US promotion trip), 'Our music scene has been dominated for a long time by the Americans, but things are gradually changing. I think that by seeing just how they do it, British artists could stay supreme at home'. A positive remark, certainly, but Kane's lofty goal was simply that British acts could rule the roost in their homeland - there was no thought of possible American success too. It seemed to be taken for granted in the early 1960s that the best a British act could aspire to was a one-off American hit, and possibly the chance of appearing low on the bill of an American rock'n'roll package show, as Cliff Richard had done in 1960. As history shows, this position almost reversed after 1964's British Invasion, when in some cases American audiences accepted UK songs more easily than their own, or only accepted US compositions when sung by British acts. In truth, during the mid and late 1960s several average UK talents were welcomed with open arms Stateside, whilst superior American artists were overlooked - a situation that would have seemed absolutely impossible throughout the period this book covers.

It's very easy to look at the music scene in those 'good old days' with only fond memories, and to forget that the era was not quite as innocent as is often imagined. If for a moment we remove those rose-coloured contact lenses we would see that those early rock years also had their ugly side - chart hyping was not unheard of, and Payola (pay for play) was rife in America. There is no doubt at all that many of the hits of the era (and indeed several since) may not have originally been played on the radio if money or goods had not

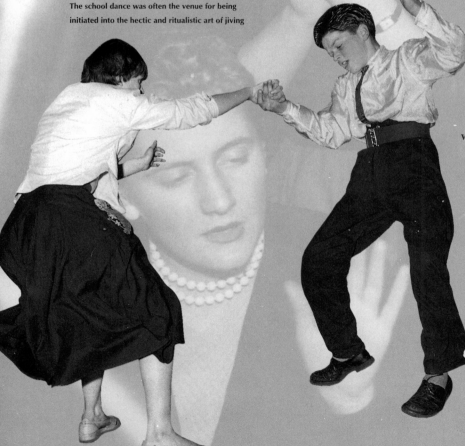

The school dance was often the venue for being initiated into the hectic and ritualistic art of jiving

changed hands! This fact naturally makes one wonder which of the 'Old Gold' hits we know and love started life this way, and which top stars may not have made the grade, if someone had not been bribed to play their early records. Equally mind-boggling is the thought that hundreds of those equally good (if not better) singles could have been played in their places. This would have resulted in sales, chart hits and successful careers for countless other talented artists who remained non-starters simply because they did not have the weight of the wallets of the major record business players behind them. Payola as such was seldom mentioned in connection with British radio, although there are stories aplenty of chart hyping occurring on both sides of the Atlantic in those formative rock years.

In closing, it would be wrong to suggest that every record mentioned in this book is worth rummaging around record sales for, but several do deserve the respect given to less original and inventive later records, and if this book helps dispel the myth that there was nothing of note musically in Britain before the Beat Boom, it has served its purpose. Additionally, if you would like to hear some of the best and most interesting British releases of the early rock era, then you could not do better than check out EMI's seven-CD series 'British Beat Before The Beatles'.

These early UK beat stars not only laid the foundations of British rock, but also built the first few storeys. Many of them were as important in the evolution of British rock as Elvis, Chuck Berry or Little Richard were in the development of rock in the USA - it is a certainty that there would have been no Beatles without the first HIT PARADE HEROES.

The last great dance craze of the Hit Parade era was the Twist

Thanks

I would like to take this opportunity of thanking Derek Brecknock, Barry Lazell, Spencer Leigh, Nora and Sandy McAleer, *NME*, Jon Philibert and of course Marty Wilde and the many performers, producers and backroom boys who have shared stories with me over the years. Also a very special thank you goes to Mike Evans, Billie Gordon and John Tobler for all their work on this project.

Softly Softly

P o p   B e f o r e   R o c k

Before the American or British beat boom of the mid-1950s, a thriving and growing music business already existed on both sides of the Atlantic, and the records produced in the first ten years after the end of World War 2 laid down the ground rules that have been followed ever since. Rock'n'roll was a combination of rhythm & blues, country & western, jazz and the general pop music of the early 1950s; the latter ingredient was as important as the former ones, and equally deserving of closer scrutiny.

Hardly a teenage heart throb, Donald Peers had one of the huge hits of the early Fifties with 'By A Babbling Brook'

After Britain had successfully resisted the invasion of Hitler's hordes and before it unconditionally surrendered to rock'n'roll, its music business was already relying heavily on input from America. Musically, Britain had no shortage of front-line troops in the late 1940s. There were the 'Forces' Sweethearts' Vera Lynn and Anne Shelton, the amiable cockney Billy Cotton and His Band, balladeers like Steve Conway (who died in 1952, aged only 31), Teddy Johnson (who also hosted the Top 20 show on Radio Luxembourg) and Donald Peers. The most successful whistler of all time, Ronnie Ronalde, was also selling 78s by the sackfull, as were dance music king Victor Silvester and The Tanner Sisters (who toured with Buddy Holly in 1958).

However, in an era when there were as many pianos in British homes as record players and sheet music still sold in the millions, it was American artists such as the unforgettable Nat 'King' Cole, Perry Como, Bing Crosby, Tony Martin, Dinah Shore and 'ol' blue eyes' Frank Sinatra, who were held in the highest esteem in Britain. The UK welcomed US talent with open arms, and yet accepted without question that its own home-grown entertainers were most unlikely to find a similarly warm welcome Stateside.

In 1952, Rosemary Clooney simultaneously claimed two of the Top 3 slots on the American chart whilst Guy Mitchell accomplished a similar feat in Britain a year later

In its last front page story of the 1940s the US music trade paper *Billboard* stated 'There is a lessening of interest in big bands' and prophesied 'in the coming decade teenage record buyers will be more influential on the popular music scene.' Apart from destroying the myth that the word 'teenager' was only coined some time later, it showed that even at that early stage the music industry were well aware that change was in the air.

In the formative years of the Fifties, there was also no shortage of new young faces being offered to an eager worldwide audience by the land of the Stars and Stripes. So many new acts were shifting shellac in 1951 that a *Billboard* headline proclaimed 'The youth movement sweeps the field.' Among the young newcomers it cited were petite teenager Teresa Brewer and the slightly older song thrushes Rosemary Clooney and Patti 'The Singing Rage' Page. Also listed amongst the new kids on the block were Boston-based quartet The Ames Brothers, Dean Martin, Philadelphia's heart-throb Eddie Fisher, Guy Mitchell, the operatic Mario Lanza and his close friend Al Martino, the first person to top the UK chart. Also classified as up-and-coming new acts were guitar ace Les Paul and his double-tracked vocalist/wife Mary Ford, vocal quartets The Four Aces and Four Knights, and influential folk group The Weavers (who included Pete Seeger).

South African-born Eve Boswell (above) hit the charts no less than three times with her jaunty 'Pickin' A Chicken', while keyboard queen Winifred Atwell started a seven-year run of hits with the patriotic 'Britannia Rag' in 1952

Food rationing was still in force in Britain, and record buyers also seemed unable to get enough good music, and not only snapped up almost everything their ex-colonial cousins could offer, but also rallied behind new home-grown talents like honky tonk pianist Winifred Atwell, comedian/singer Max Bygraves, Frank Chacksfield and His Orchestra, ex-Ted Heath Band vocalists Lita Roza and Dickie Valentine, mixed quintet The Stargazers (the first group to top the British chart), high kickin' Frankie Vaughan, David Whitfield and Jimmy Young, now a top-rated radio presenter. It was in the early 1950s that screaming at pop stars became a regular pastime for teenage girls, even on the seemingly sedate European side of the Atlantic. Neither Valentine nor Vaughan were strangers to screaming hordes, but it was their American counterparts, big-voiced Frankie Laine and his Columbia label-mate Johnnie Ray, who created near hysteria at their shows. Ray particularly, whose repertoire included semi-suggestive songs like 'Such A Night', was mobbed almost every-where he played and was often semi-stripped by souvenir-seeking supporters in those days just before beat blossomed and rock ruled.

As for the songs themselves, at a time when they were arguably more important than their singers, few British writ-ers could hope to match their American Tin Pan Alley counter-parts. Since the 1920s the songsmiths serving Hollywood and Broadway seemed to have patented the art of international hit writing, and at least 75 per cent of the United Kingdom's most popular songs of the early 1950s had travelled across the Atlantic.

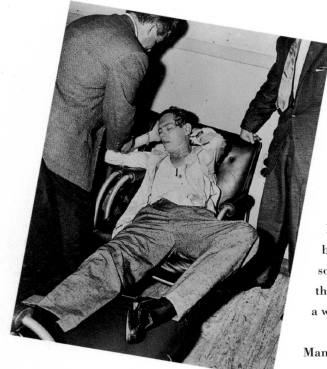

Dubbed by the press – and his own publicity – as the 'Cry Guy', the 'Nabob of Sob' and the 'Prince of Wails', Johnnie Ray's emotional stage-act had the fans literally trying to tear the clothes off his back .

It was commonplace then for a good song to be snapped up by at least a handful of artists on both sides of the Atlantic and, unlike nowadays, it was certainly not unusual for an act to release several singles in a matter of weeks. From this it is clear that the now forsaken marketing plan known as 'throw enough mud at the wall' was the norm, and it does not seem to have worried artists, or their fans, that not every record they released was a hit - the charts and an artist's 100 per cent track record had yet to be deemed as important as they were to be in the rock'n'roll era. Record companies obviously put their muscle behind most records but it would appear that as long as an artist sold large quantities of some of their singles everyone was reasonably happy. It was a time in the music business when the saying 'you win some, you lose some' was a way of life.

Many people simply dismiss pre-rock songs as a mixture of naivety and novelties – which is an unfair judgement. That's not to suggest the love songs of that time would be considered streetwise today. However, they were as perfect for the period as Madonna's 'Hanky Panky' or 'Erotica' were for the early 1990s, and the relative innocence of some of these older songs makes that era

more attractive in retrospect. Every year has its novelty hits and some of the biggest selling examples have come in the rock era. But there were probably more songs in this vein released in the ten years after World War 2 than at any similar period, but who can criticise the public for wanting a little light relief after being involved in

Frankie Laine's

macho mix of

religious ballads

like 'I Believe' and

'Answer Me' and

tall-in-the-saddle

cowboy songs were

kitsch classics of

their day

In 1951 Miss Patti Page had three singles concurrently in the Top 10 and for a few weeks Tony Bennett held the top two places on the US chart, a feat Johnnie Ray repeated early in 1952

In 1954, two versions of the theme from from the film *Limelight*, composed by Charlie Chaplin, were present together in the UK Top 3

Frankie Laine's recording of 'I Believe' spent 18 weeks at No. 1 and his version of 'Answer Me' shared the top spot with a cover version by David Whitfield

such a long and bloody conflict? And what's so wrong with lightweight fun songs like 'If I Knew You Were Comin' I'd've Baked A Cake', 'The Thing' (which is derived from an old English ballad called 'The Chandler's Wife'),'How Much Is That Doggie In The Window', 'I See The Moon', 'Where Will The Baby's Dimple Be' and 'I Taught I Taw A Puddy Tat' ? It's also worth remembering, when considering the content of many pre-rock'n'roll lyrics, that the world had more infants growing up than at any previous time, and many of the songs were written to appeal to the thousands of families with young offspring.

These were the days when 95 per cent of pop singers had to rely on professional songwriters for their material - the age of the self-contained singer/songwriter was still in the distant future. The writers, like most of those who followed in their wake, wanted to pen hits and make as much money as possible. The fact that in the early 1950s the appetites of most transatlantic record buyers for lightweight pop and good

TOP SINGLES 1956

❶ PAT BOONE
I'll Be Home
London American

JOHNNY RAY ❷
Just Walkin' In The Rain
Philips

❸ DORIS DAY
Whatever Will Be Will Be
Philips

FRANKIE LAINE ❹
A Woman In Love
Philips

❺ RONNIE HILTON
No Other Love
HMV

novelty songs seemed insatiable, meant that this was part of the basic diet that 'Tin Pan Alley' and the record business fed them, until such a time that the public demanded more roughage in their musical menu.

As a mini memory jerker for readers who remember the Festival of Britain and the days when King George VI was on the throne, the top sheet music sellers of 1950-5 in Britain were the C&W-oriented 'Jealous Heart' in 1950, the light operatic 'Be My Love' in 1951, and 'Auf Wiederseh'n Sweetheart', which was popularised by Vera Lynn with the help of 70 servicemen in 1952. Outselling the competition in 1953 was the semi-religious ballad 'I Believe', and in 1954 it was the turn of the German children's song 'Happy Wanderer'. The only 100 per cent British song to top the year's sheet music chart was 'Softly, Softly', a big hit for Ruby Murray in 1955.

In March 1955, soft-voiced Ruby Murray had five singles in the Top Twenty at the same time, including her biggest smash 'Softly Softly' and the tear-jerker 'If Anyone Finds This I Love You'

In May 1951 two records entered the American R&B chart that are often cited as the first genuine rock'n'roll tracks: Jackie Brenston's 'Rocket 88' and the Dominoes' 'Sixty Minute Man'. Meanwhile country and western acts Johnnie Lee Willis and Tommy Scott released 'This Band's A Rockin'' and 'Rockin' And Rollin'' respectively, and in Britain Tennessee Ernie Ford was heading into the Top 5 with 'Shotgun Boogie'.

When the Teddy Boys appeared on the scene just a year or so before rock'n'roll, it was clear things were never going to be the same again

Before major record companies realised there was money to be made by sanitising R&B music, they had been dipping into Country and Western song catalogues for some years. Tex Williams had topped the American pop chart in 1947 with the country-style novelty 'Smoke! Smoke! Smoke! (That Cigarette)' and by the close of the decade western tunes like 'Riders In The Sky' and 'Mule Train' had also become huge transatlantic hits. Once the major labels realised there was gold in them thar hillbillies, the floodgates really opened, and in the early 1950s C&W copyrights like 'Tennessee Waltz', 'Jealous Heart', 'Rag Mop', 'Slow Poke' (known as 'Slow Coach' in Britain) and 'Chattanooga Shoe Shine Boy' were all big transatlantic hits. Occasionally it would be the original country records that crossed over to the pop charts, but more often than not the hit recordings would be de-countrified, polished up and transformed by established pop artists, which not surprisingly made them more palatable to the general public. As their R&B cousins would realise later, such pop covers may be bad news for the original artists but are certainly good news for writers and publishers, bringing far more money into the coffers than they could ever have earned with merely a (usually regionally successful) country hit. As might be expected, it was Hank Williams, more than any other writer, whose songs were found to be most suitable for this 'pop-ularising' treatment. At the height of his fame, pop singers literally lined up to cover both sides of any new Williams release. His record label, MGM, would even advertise Hank's single on the same page as their own pop covers of both sides. Significantly there is no record of Hank Williams complaining about the ads – or the fact that he earned a large proportion of his income from other artists performing his songs.

In the year or so before rock'n'roll planted its initially shallow roots, Britain had welcomed to its ranks of best-selling pop artists such ballad singers as Ronnie Hilton (another successful radio presenter in the Nineties), Gary Miller and Malcolm Vaughan, and on the distaff side, the vivacious Alma Cogan and the 20-year-old Irish sensation Ruby Murray, who broke all records before and since when five of her singles were simultaneously situated in the Top 20. They were a formidable collection, but again it was the newer American artists that the British public placed on an even higher pedestal. Numbered amongst these new US pop idols were ballad-belter Don Cornell, Country&Western yodeller Slim Whitman (whose 'Rose Marie' headed the chart for 11 successive weeks) and vocal groups The Chordettes, The Crew Cuts and The McGuire Sisters, whose records hinted at the beat music revolution that was just around the corner.

In 1954 Joan Weber broke the US sales record when her version of the C&W song, 'Let Me Go Lover' (originally an anti-drink song called 'Let Me Go Devil'), sold 500,000 in one week

Alma Cogan was as well known for her flamboyant frocks as for such memorable songs as 'Twenty Tiny Fingers', 'Willie Can' and 'Never Do A Tango With An Eskimo'

Two versions of 'The Third Man Theme' and 'Harbor Lights' held the top couple of rungs on the US chart in 1950, and in the same year Gordon Jenkins had three separate sides simultaneously in the Top 10

The Great Pretenders

Ham Rock and Sham Rock

Ray Ellington (above) featured on the sheet music of one of his recordings 'You Gotta Love Everybody'

Ted Heath (below) with actress Mylene Demongeot and his singer Dennis Lotis, discussing the 1956 film 'It's A Wonderful World' in which they all appeared

Most British A&R (artists & repertoire) men in the first half of the 1950s dismissed R&B and Country & Western as musical trends whose appeal was probably limited to either black Americans or cowboys, and therefore seldom checked out new releases for possible songs that homegrown acts could cover. However, their continual search for US songs as vehicles for their artists to record occasionally led to a British singer or band covering a copyright that had started life in the R&B or C&W backwaters rather than in 'Tin Pan Alley' or on Broadway.

Ray Ellington, one of the few black recording artists in Britain in the 1950s, was probably the first act to regularly record songs from the R&B and C&W areas, albeit in a jazz-based style. He covered such diversified compositions as Louis Jordan's hit 'Let The Good Times Roll' in 1951, and Hank Williams' ode to a wooden Indian, 'Kaw-Liga', a couple of years later. Ellington's records were not slavish copies; he had a style of his own, and professed, 'I don't want to be a carbon copy of any American idol, I want to be judged on my own merits.' Ellington's quartet, who recorded over 70 sides in the 1950s, were a very popular live act and always fared well in popularity polls, although curiously they never charted.

In those days of demob suits and debutantes, the British public liked nothing better than dancing to big band music, be it at the local Palais, a party or simply at home in front of the ubiquitous gramophone. It was deemed the duty of the bands to keep the populace on the ballroom floor, which occasionally meant that they would play and, in some cases record, a rock-oriented tune, to satisfy the growing legion of youthful jivers. Amongst these early examples of UK rock-related recordings were two 1953 covers of Bill Haley & The Comets' first US hit, 'Crazy Man Crazy', by the Oscar Rabin Band and Ted Heath's Orchestra.

By 1954 British A&R men, bands and singers were looking much closer at R&B music (albeit often via the American pop cover) as a source of hit material. Popular ex-Ted Heath Band vocalist Dennis Lotis covered Johnnie Ray's suggestive single, 'Such A Night' (originally recorded by R&B group The Drifters), and The Johnston Brothers recorded The Crew Cuts' novelty hit, 'Sh-Boom' (first released by R&B group The Chords), and coupled it with their treatment of The Crew Cuts' original 'Crazy 'Bout You Baby'. Mr & Mrs Smith's five boys, The Five Smith Brothers, were also early passengers on the rock bandwagon, attemping Bill Haley's 'A.B.C. Boogie'. Three less likely rock acts than South Africa born Lotis and the brothers Johnston and Smith would be hard to imagine. As the year ended, a British-produced version of 'Shake, Rattle & Roll' by 1940s-styled US pop/ gospel group The Deep River Boys fought an unsuccessful battle in UK record shops with Bill Haley's recording of the song, which (in its uncensored form) had originally been a hit in the R&B charts by 'boss of the blues' Joe Turner.

Many music historians name 1955 as the year when rock's reign started and all other forms of popular music hastily retreated. But it was certainly not that way in Britain, where the old guard were still well in control. The year may have ended with 'Rock Around The Clock' in the No. 1 spot, but the music establishment and the media refused to surrender any ground to this onslaught from overseas. Unlike their American equivalents, UK labels were not rushing to recruit 'untrained and untalented singers', and the rock'n'roll craze was getting minimum column inches of press coverage. It was still generally thought that rock music, like America's other contribution to culture in 1955, Davy Crockett, would simply be a short-lived novelty that the public would soon reject, and all the record companies had to do to ride out this rocky storm was record these 'novelty' songs with established British artists. Among the more bizarre singles released using this formula were Jill Day's cover of Gale Storm's US hit, 'I Hear You Knockin'' (originally an R&B hit for Smiley Lewis), and Suzi Miller's versions of Georgia Gibbs' US charters 'Tweedle Dee' (first recorded by LaVern Baker) and 'Dance With Me Henry' (a cleaned-up version of Etta James' No. 1 R&B hit, 'The Wallflower', which contained the more dubious hook line, 'Roll With Me Henry'). British bands, too, were recording some unexpected covers, such as Ronnie Aldrich's 'Ko-Ko-Mo' (a Perry Como hit that started life as an R&B track by Gene & Eunice), Ted Heath's version of the classic show closer 'Goodnight Sweetheart' (a US Top 10 entry for the McGuire Sisters that had been cut originally by R&B group The Spaniels), and Billy Cotton's version of the catchy up-tempo gem 'Hearts Of Stone'. This last had been a US No. 1 for The Fontane Sisters, who had covered The Charms' R&B chart topper, which itself was a cover of The Jewels' original recording! Britain was receiving its rock third-hand and sometimes even fourth-hand, and any connection between rock'n'roll and most of the above British records was purely coincidental.

One of the great originals of jazz-based rhythm and blues, Louis Jordan; his 'jump jive' sound was a direct influence on the likes of Ray Ellington and a true forerunner of rock'n'roll

Throughout the Fifties Ted Heath and his Music, along with resident singers like Lita Roza, topped the bill wherever they played, be it concert halls, ballrooms or theatres

The closest the United Kingdom came to the 'real thing' that year were records by Jamaican quartet The Southlanders, who covered the doo-wop anthem 'Earth Angel', and Don Lang, a jazz-based trombone player and vocalist, who charted with the tongue-twister 'Cloudburst'. Another interesting locally produced record was the Deep River Boys' version of 'Rock Around The Clock'. The group even appeared on TV with 1940s forces' favourite and ukelele maestro George Formby, demonstrating how rock'n'roll was nothing new as it had the same beat as songs from the past like 'Sweet Georgia Brown'.

Across the Atlantic, 1955 was the year McDonalds sold their first hamburger, Disneyland admitted its first customer, and Alan Freed's all-star rock/R&B package shows were packing them in coast to coast. In contrast, England's teens and twenties thronged to the Royal Albert Hall to watch BBC's *Festival Of Dance Music*, and to the first pop concert (*NME* Poll Winners) ever staged at the Royal Albert Hall. They watched the top names in British music such as the bands of Ted Heath, Cyril Stapleton and Ken Mackintosh, Geraldo & His Orchestra, and vocalists Dickie Valentine, Alma Cogan, Frankie Vaughan, Joan Regan, Max Bygraves and The Stargazers - nary a rocker in sight. As fans mobbed Valentine and cheered themselves hoarse for Heath, few could have realised that things would never be quite the same again. As 1955 closed, Cyril Stapleton's successful *Show Band* TV series ended with top UK group, the cheerful and clean-cut Stargazers, singing 'Rock Around The Clock'. It was an omen of things to come.

January 1956 found Lonnie Donegan, the banjo player in Chris Barber's traditional jazz band, with a hit single in his own right, 'Rock Island Line'. This was the record that introduced skiffle music to the British public and its success Stateside (where it reached the Top 10) showed that British beat records could sell in the land that gave birth to rock. However, as Donegan's producer Alan A. Freeman warned, 'If we are ever to make records that sound on a par with American hits, we must become more original and create better ideas and gimmicks ourselves.'

When the Ted Heath Band returned from their first US tour in May 1956, they were grilled by a music media now desperate to know more about rock. Heath's opinion was that 'Rock'n'roll is mainly performed by coloured artists for coloured people, and is therefore unlikely to be popular here'. This did not seem so unlikely at the time. After all there were no *a capella* vocal groups doo-wopping on British street corners, and only a small black population, who were far more interested in West

Indian calypso music. Unlike their American counterparts, young British people had not grown up listening to a diet of either R&B or country music and it was presumed therefore that their interest in rock, which combined the two, would last no longer than that for the mambo, the other US musical craze of the time.

When it became clear that rock was not ready to recede, interest in it as a source of coverable songs grew rapidly in the UK, and 1956 saw many more of the old-school singers and musicians boarding the big-beat bandwagon. Top-line female artists like Alma Cogan (who claimed to have recorded Britain's first rock'n'roll jingle), Billie Anthony, Marion Ryan and even veterans like Gracie Fields and Anne Shelton incorporated a little rock into their repertoires, as did balladeers like Dickie Valentine, Ray Burns, Lee Lawrence and Benny Lee. Groups such as The Four Jones Boys and The Kentones also added a dash of rock, as did the orchestras of Joe Loss and Ron Goodwin, *NME* poll winners The Kirchins, and even Big Ben's Banjo Band released a couple of rock'n'roll medleys before 1956 was out.

During the summer of 1956 interest in rock was escalating, and the search was on in earnest for a genuine home-grown rock'n'roll act. In August London's first rock music club, Studio 51, opened with Rory Blackwell's Rock & Rollers headlining, while in Manchester new Columbia Records signings ex-jazz drummer Tony Crombie & His Rockets made their stage debut, and a month later The Goons (Peter Sellers, Harry Secombe and Spike Milligan) charted with the comedy novelty 'Bloodnok's Rock n Roll'. October found more British jazz musicians rocking and rolling. Sax man Red Price announced he was forming a rock group within the Ted Heath Band; Art Baxter (who had sung with Ronnie Scott's Band) & His Rockin' Sinners and ex-Tubby Hayes vocalist Bobby Breen & His Rock 'n' Roll Rockers hit the road, and Kenny Flame & The Rockets starred with balladeer Ronnie Harris in the show *Rock Around The Town*. It's quite possible that some of these performers were sincere would-be rockers, and it may be unfair to dismiss them simply as jazz musicians who were trying to enhance their bank balances. Whatever, the public did not really take to them. The *NME* at the time explained that 'British fans usually only accept rock'n'roll from a genuine rock artist, not from somebody who is merely cashing in on the craze', adding: 'As yet we have not got the beat right in this country.'

On October 19 the first local rock record charted: 'Teach You To Rock'/ 'Short'nin' Bread' by Tony Crombie & His Rockets. A week later 19-year-old Londoner Tommy

For better or worse, Tommy Steele was certainly the first genuine rock'n'roll star to appear on the British pop scene in the Fifties

Steele became the first British rock act to reach the Top 20, and he did it with an original song, 'Rock With The Caveman'. British beat was born.

RAY ELLINGTON

Ellington, the London-born son of an American father and Russian mother, played drums in various bands in the 1940s, and backed such notables as Fats Waller when they worked in the UK. He formed the Ray Ellington Quartet in 1948, and they debuted at the London Palladium on a bill with the Ted Heath Orchestra. Ellington started recording on Parlophone in 1950, and in that era also appeared on Decca, Columbia, Pye and Ember. His recording repertoire was varied, and included pop novelties and covers of such notable songs as 'Earth Angel' (originally by The Penguins), 'Two Hearts' (Pat Boone's first hit, which had been initially recorded by The Charms), 'Giddy Up A Ding Dong' (first heard in the film *Rock Around The Clock* sung by Freddie Bell & The Bellboys), the comical Leiber & Stoller song 'Charlie Brown' (originally by The Cues, and later a hit for The Coasters) and 'Green Door' (Jim Lowe's US hit). He also cut more obscure R&B hits like The Jayhawks' 'Stranded In The Jungle', The Robins' 'Framed', Ray Bryant's oft-recorded dance track 'The Madison' and singer/songwriter Terry Gilkyson's catchy pop/calypso hit 'Marianne'. His quartet was best known in that era as the resident band on the top-rated radio programme, *The Goon Show*, and the humorous Ellington often took part in the actual shows. His records never reached the Top 30 (the yardstick at the time) but he was arguably the first UK act to regularly record R&B and rock'n'roll material. His son Lance was a critically acclaimed singer in the late 1980s.

Ray Ellington, leading his Quartet in front of a packed audience at the Plaza Ballroom, Manchester, in 1953

Radio compatriots of Ray Ellington, the Goons had Top Five smashes in 1956 with 'I'm Walking Backwards For Christmas' and 'Ying Tong Song'

TED HEATH ORCHESTRA

Before forming his own band in 1944, London-born Ted Heath (not to be confused with a 1970s British Prime Minister!) had played trombone with the bill-topping bands of Jack Hylton, Ambrose and Geraldo. Heath's band introduced the public to many musicians who later led their own bands, such as Kenny Baker, Stanley Black, Jack Parnell and Ronnie Scott, and vocalists Dickie Valentine, Lita Roza and Dennis Lotis all became solo stars after building their reputations with the outfit. The poll-winning ensemble was the most popular British band on both sides of the Atlantic in the 1950s. In America his albums always sold well, and his shows were often sell-outs. In fact, *Billboard* described them as 'having no rivals in the commercial dance band field.' Whatever the new musical trend, Heath's band would attempt to incorporate it into their repertoire. So, during the mid 1950s, this jazz-based outfit recorded mambos, cha chas and rock'n'roll numbers. On the rock side, Heath's recordings included the bass guitar and sax-heavy instrumental 'Raunchy' (originally by Bill Justis), 'Rock & Roll Waltz' (a US hit for Kay Starr), the Latin rocker 'Tequila' (an American No. 1 for The Champs) and 'Madison Time' (first cut by Al Brown). He kept most of his original fans throughout the era but, despite regular appearances on the teen-TV show *6. 5 Special*, few younger record buyers accepted the band as the 'real thing'.

Ted Heath leads his roaring big band; note vocalists Dickie Valentine and Lita Roza seated in front of the Orchestra, patiently 'waiting their turn' to sing

SOUTHLANDERS

The Southlanders were the nearest thing Britain had to a rock'n'roll vocal group in the mid-1950s. The quartet, which consisted of Vernon Nesbith, Frank Mannah and brothers Alan and Harry Wilmot, first met and sang together when serving in the Royal Air Force during World War 2. After the war the members returned home to Jamaica and made a name for themselves there. Needing a new challenge, they returned to Britain in 1953 and before long had a record deal with Parlophone, playing with top acts like Geraldo and Frankie Vaughan. By 1957, the time of their only chart hit, 'Alone' (a distinctive cover of the Shepherd Sisters' singalong US hit), they had also established a reputation in Germany, Italy, France and Belgium, had starred at London's noted night spot the Astor Club and had become familiar faces on *6.5 Special*. Their other interesting releases included covers of Fats Domino's 'Ain't That A Shame', The Penguins' 'Earth Angel', Little Joe & The Thrillers' 'Peanuts' and New York group The Voxpoppers' 'Wishing For Your Love', though they are arguably better known for their recording of the US novelty

TOP SINGLES 1957

1. PAUL ANKA
Diana
Columbia

2. ELVIS PRESLEY
All Shook Up
HMV

3. TAB HUNTER
Young Love
London American

4. HARRY BELAFONTE
Mary's Boy Child
RCA

5. LONNIE DONEGAN
Cumberland Gap
Pye Nixa

23••

song, 'The Mole In A Hole'. Harry Wilmot's son, Gary, is now a well-known TV personality in the UK.

Don Lang, and in the background some of the Frantic Five, complete with trombone and what became something of a trademark, his *6-5 Special* jacket

DON LANG

Don Lang was born Gordon Langhorn in Halifax. He played trombone in various bands including those led by Peter Rose, Teddy Foster, Vic Lewis (where he was part of a progressive modern jazz section) and Ken Mackintosh (he played on 'The Creep'). Together with his Frantic Five, he was the most regularly featured act on *6.5 Special*, and it was his version of the theme song that is best remembered. With his *6.5 Special* baseball jacket and short greasy hair he looked like a mature US college student. This image was not helped by the fact that he played the unfashionable trombone and sang in a semi-scat style. He charted with cover versions of Claud Cloud's 'Cloudburst', Chuck Berry's anthemic rocker 'School Day' and the novelty 'Witch Doctor', which, like the original by David Seville, included a speeded up voice gimmick. Among his unsuccessful singles were versions of Guy Mitchell's chart-topping 'Rock-A-Billy', Don Rondo's US hit 'White Silver Sands', The Champs' 'Tequila' and Bobby Darin's rocking name-dropper, 'Queen Of The Hop'. He later sang with MOR stalwarts, the Mike Sammes Singers and the Cliff Adams Singers, and at the time of his death in 1991 was successfully playing rock 'n'roll revival shows. He was held in high esteem by many UK rock fans including Beatles John and George, who used him on the' White Album'. However, it could be argued that he was a square peg trying to force himself into a round hole.

RORY BLACKWELL

The speeded-up vocal break on David Seville's original of 'Witchdoctor' provided the formula for Seville's string of smashes with The Chipmunks

Rory Blackwell was a pioneer of British rock'n'roll. Despite the fact that he did not appear on record until the summer of 1957, Rory Blackwell and The Rock & Rollers had been the headliners at the launch of London's first rock club, Studio 51, a year earlier. His only record release in the early rock era was a cover of The Everly Brothers' US Top 3 hit, 'Bye Bye Love', which failed to dent the sales of the Kentucky duo's version in Britain. He built up a reputation entertaining holidaymakers at Butlin's camps, many of whom had never seen a rock'n'roll singer before, and he so influenced Liverpool singer Alan Caldwell that he changed his name to Rory Storm in his honour (Storm led the Hurricanes, whose drummer was Ringo Starr). In recent years Blackwell, who like Screamin' Lord Sutch and Wee Willie Harris is forever a showman, has reputedly broken the world record for non-stop drumming.

KEN MACKINTOSH

This Halifax-born saxophonist, who played in the bands of George Elrick and Oscar Rabin, formed his own orchestra in 1948. They were the resident band at Nottingham's Astoria ballroom until 1950 when they were invited to be the opening attraction at the prestigious Wimbledon Palais in London. He and the band signed to HMV, and they first charted with their original version of the big dance hit 'The Creep', in early 1954. Mackintosh's band was a top drawing card throughout the 1950s and they returned to the Top 20 in 1958 with a version of the Bill Justis rock-instrumental, 'Raunchy'. He hoped the success of that record meant that 'kids would demand a more solid sound than skiffle, which gets monotonous after a few hours.' Mackintosh aimed 'to keep pace with changing tastes and balance his show between what the teenagers and the older people wanted.' In order to reach a younger audience, the band often appeared on *6.5 Special*, but they were a little too long in the tooth to attract many new fans. Mackintosh admitted 'There won't be a return to the old powerhouse days. The rock beat is here to stay.' He was right.

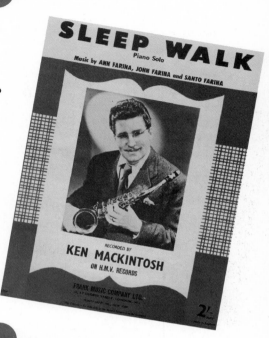

Self-confessed band-waggoner Ken Mackintosh covered the hit instrumental 'Sleep Walk', which charted on both sides of the Atlantic in its American original by Santo and Johnny

TONY CROMBIE

The London-born bebop drummer was a well-known figure on the British modern jazz scene in the late 1940s and 1950s. He backed many visiting American vocal artists including Lena Horne and Carmen McRae, played in the prestigious bands of Ronnie Scott and Victor Feldman, and the Tony Crombie Orchestra was voted into the Top 10 of the small bands category by *NME* readers in 1954. In 1956 he formed what is generally considered to be the very first British-based rock'n'roll group, The Rockets (as their name suggests, they loosely modelled themselves on Bill Haley & The Comets), who included Rex Morris, Jimmy Currie (soon to be playing with Lonnie Donegan), Ashley Kozak and Clyde Ray. Their recording of Freddie Bell & The Bell Boys' 'Teach You To Rock', which is regarded as the first British rock hit - it spent two weeks in the Top Thirty - was produced by Norrie Paramor (who accumulated over two dozen chart toppers in his career with artists like Cliff Richard, Helen Shapiro and Frank Ifield). Later recordings like 'Rock Rock Rock' (both originally by Jimmy Cavallo & His Houserockers), 'We're Gonna Rock Tonight' (which Teddy Randazzo and The Chuckles had previously cut) and originals like 'London Rock', 'Brighton Rock', and 'Sham Rock' indicated the market at which Crombie was desperately aiming, and perhaps the last title best summed up these records. By the end of the decade, he had forsaken rock'n'roll forever and returned to Ronnie Scott's crew-cutted jazz group.

The original US version of 'Raunchy' by Bill Justis peaked at Number Two in November 1957

Rock Britannia

Home-grown Heroes

Tommy Steele was not only Britain's first real rock star, he was also the most important and significant home-grown discovery until the arrival of Cliff Richard, and arguably the most innovative UK rock'n'roll act of the1950s. He was very different from the vast majority of British pop stars who preceded him, dressing and talking - at least initially - like an ordinary bloke (to use his cockney parlance): Steele was Britain's first working-class rock hero. Perhaps more importantly, in a land where cover versions were as common as chip shops and singer/songwriters as scarce as supermarkets, he not only recorded many of his own rock compositions but performed them in a uniquely British manner. Thanks to his very shrewd management, within weeks of first charting in October 1956 with his single 'Rock With The Caveman', he was sufficiently well known to be voted one of Britain's Top 10 Male Singers in the *NME* Poll. And even though his rush-released follow-up, 'Doomsday Rock', failed to chart, he became so famous that a couple of months later his life story was being filmed! Steele's next two singles had originally been recorded by C&W star Marty Robbins, and had both been covered for the US pop market by Guy Mitchell. The first, 'Singing The Blues', reached the top of the UK chart for both Mitchell and Steele, but Mitchell grabbed the majority of the sales on the follow-up, 'Knee Deep In The Blues'.

Critics slammed rock, the majority of the public scorned it, and despite its success, most representatives of the UK record business disliked it and considered it a flash-in-the-pan. Therefore much of the UK music industry breathed a sigh of relief when the US trade paper *Cash Box* reported in early 1957, 'The type of r'n'r that originally excited kids has quietly receded into the background, and has been replaced by a softer version with more emphasis on melody and lyric.' In Britain, *NME* noticed: 'The initial impact of the big beat has worn away and asked 'Is rock'n'roll on the way out or growing up?'

Thanks firstly to ATV's *Cool For Cats*, and then to the BBC's *6.5 Special*, rock reached into millions of British homes in 1957, and those television shows helped create many hits and added several more stars to the UK's expanding r'n'r galaxy. The first of these was teenager Terry Dene, a singer apparently cast in the Presley mould. Dene, like Tommy Steele, recorded several original rock'n'roll compositions and also twice raided Marty Robbins' repertoire. Stardom worried Dene, who was only 18 when his debut single 'A White Sports Coat' charted. 'When I read

By the time his second film *The Duke Wore Jeans* came out, Tommy Steele was already well on the way to becoming more than just a poor man's Elvis Presley

that I am a star', he moaned, 'it panics me, because I've got to live up to that and act like a star.' He never managed to cope with being a teenage idol, and more traumatically with being a has-been before he was even 21. He was the first real human casualty of British rock.

Meanwhile Lonnie Donegan and Elvis Presley both scored their first No. 1 singles and Tommy Steele collected the fourth of his 13 UK Top 20 hits with his composition 'Butterfingers', which, like 'Doomsday Rock', was a regional success in the US. Such was the American interest that in 1957 he had offers to appear on both Ed Sullivan's show and Patti Page's successful TV programme, 'The Big Record'. Probably wisely, he turned down these initial approaches, insisting that he would not go to the US to promote his records 'unless it was a good proposition, and things were done our way.' He knew what the likely reaction to a British rock'n'roller would be Stateside, and, as he put it, ' I don't want to go there and die a million deaths.' When his record selling days were over in the United Kingdom, Steele, who had evolved into a family entertainer in the best tradition of the British music hall and variety stage, received the offer he had been waiting for and headed for Hollywood, where he starred in several musicals.

Noted for his checked shirts at the time, Jim Dale in the television studio for *6-5 Special*

6.5 Special also played a large part in the success of singer/ songwriter Russ Hamilton, 13-year-old Laurie London and singer/actor Jim Dale. Hamilton's first single, 'We Will Make Love', initially described as British hillbilly, was released on the independent label Oriole. It not only took him into the Top 3, but its B-side, 'Rainbow', reached the US Top 10. Schoolboy London was even more successful in America, where his rousing revival of the spiritual, 'He's Got The Whole World In His Hands', reached No. 2. Jim Dale's happy personality helped push his version of 'Be My Girl' into the runner-up position on the chart. It was a cover version of an unsuccessful US record by Johnny Madara which, like Dale's recording, was released by EMI. Dale, who never saw himself as just a rock'n'roll singer, uttered what would soon become a cliché among pop stars: 'I want to stay in the business, so I aim to make myself an all-round entertainer.' His aim was good and he has had one of the most successful careers of any 1950s UK hit-maker, as a stage actor and film star.

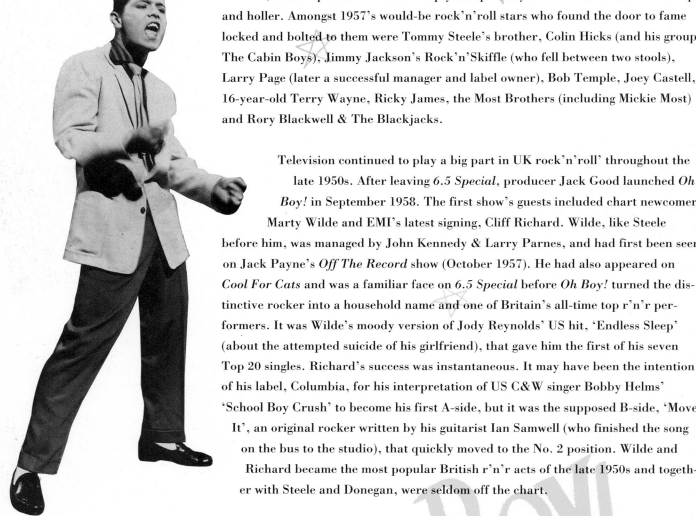

The youthful – some would say
he's ever-youthful – Cliff Richard,
singing live on the *Oh Boy!* television show

Home-grown British rockers may have been scarcer than a fog-free November in London, but the public would not simply accept everyone who could shake their hips and holler. Amongst 1957's would-be rock'n'roll stars who found the door to fame locked and bolted to them were Tommy Steele's brother, Colin Hicks (and his group The Cabin Boys), Jimmy Jackson's Rock'n'Skiffle (who fell between two stools), Larry Page (later a successful manager and label owner), Bob Temple, Joey Castell, 16-year-old Terry Wayne, Ricky James, the Most Brothers (including Mickie Most) and Rory Blackwell & The Blackjacks.

Television continued to play a big part in UK rock'n'roll' throughout the late 1950s. After leaving *6.5 Special*, producer Jack Good launched *Oh Boy!* in September 1958. The first show's guests included chart newcomer Marty Wilde and EMI's latest signing, Cliff Richard. Wilde, like Steele before him, was managed by John Kennedy & Larry Parnes, and had first been seen on Jack Payne's *Off The Record* show (October 1957). He had also appeared on *Cool For Cats* and was a familiar face on *6.5 Special* before *Oh Boy!* turned the distinctive rocker into a household name and one of Britain's all-time top r'n'r performers. It was Wilde's moody version of Jody Reynolds' US hit, 'Endless Sleep' (about the attempted suicide of his girlfriend), that gave him the first of his seven Top 20 singles. Richard's success was instantaneous. It may have been the intention of his label, Columbia, for his interpretation of US C&W singer Bobby Helms' 'School Boy Crush' to become his first A-side, but it was the supposed B-side, 'Move It', an original rocker written by his guitarist Ian Samwell (who finished the song on the bus to the studio), that quickly moved to the No. 2 position. Wilde and Richard became the most popular British r'n'r acts of the late 1950s and together with Steele and Donegan, were seldom off the chart.

The house band on *Oh Boy!*, Lord Rockingham's XI, were the next act to dart into the chart. Britain's first real rocking big band was the brainchild of Jack Good and musical arranger Harry Robinson (who had previously recorded with acts like Jim Dale and Jackie Dennis). The public loved the exuberant band's 'Hoots Mon', complete with its broad Scottish narrative from Robinson. It became the first British composition performed by a British group to reach No. 1.

6.5 Special still had a lot of influence on British record buyers in 1958, and it can claim responsibility for launching the short but spectacular career of kilted 15-year-old Jackie Dennis, who hit the high spots with his debut single 'La Dee Dah' (a cover of Billie & Lillie's US Top 20 entry). Like his Decca label-mate Steele, Dennis had excellent management who amassed massive media coverage for the precocious singer. However he did not have Steele's talent and was left behind as rock rolled on. In July 1958, *6.5 Special* played a mystery version of Bobby Darin's first US hit 'Splish Splash' - with vocals as wild as anything yet heard from a British performer. The reason for the secrecy was that the singer was the well-known slapstick comedian Charlie Drake. The record beat the original version up the chart, and to prove it was no fluke, Drake later released some equally convincing rock'n'roll follow-ups including covers of 'Itchy Twitchy Feeling' (originally by Bobby Hendricks) and 'Sea Cruise' (a US Top 20 hit by Frankie Ford).

Billy Fury was the most important rock idol launched by *Oh Boy!* in 1959. Unlike most British singers, Fury wrote many of the songs he recorded, including his first four chart entries 'Maybe Tomorrow', 'Margo', 'Colette' and 'That's Love'. He remained extremely popular throughout the early 1960s and in total managed to put 18 singles into the Top 20.

The Presley-inspired stage performances of both Cliff Richard and Fury initially shocked many viewers. Remember that at this time Elvis had never been seen performing live on UK television and the blatantly sexual presentations of Cliff and Billy often got them panned in the press, which of course increased their already fast growing fan followings. The noted *NME* journalist Alley Cat, who was a supporter of rock'n'roll, described a 1958 appearance by Richard as 'the most crude exhibitionism ever seen on British TV. His violent hip swinging during an obvious attempt to copy Elvis was revolting.' Richard's fifth single, the Lionel Bart-penned ballad 'Living Doll', introduced him to an older audience. Richard admitted he was 'thrilled to know my horizons are expanding, and would like to continue to broaden my musical outlook, so that I can reach even more people.' In hindsight, rock critics rightfully credit Fury with recording some of the best r'n'r to ever come out of Britain, but it should not be forgotten when accolades are awarded that Richard's recordings like 'High Class Baby' (which he considered 'a horrible record that deserves to be forgotten'), 'Dynamite' and his version of Billy The Kid's 'Apron Strings' were among the best early British rock tracks.

Children's television star Charlie Drake – he was part of a slapstick duo called Mick and Montmorency – had by far the unlikeliest image for a rock hit-maker, while on the other hand Billy Fury's moody good looks (below) seemed tailor-made for the role of contemporary teen idol

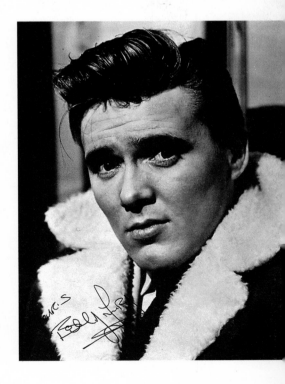

By 1959 many of the new UK recording artists were second generation rockers, basing their sound, performance, style and image more on late 1950s UK and US rock/pop artists than on the wild early American rock role models who had influenced Steele, Wilde, Richard and Fury. There were, however, exceptions to the rule in those run-up years to the Beatles era and Johnny Kidd & The Pirates were undoubtedly the best known of these. Their debut single, a Kidd original, 'Please Don't Touch', reached the Top 20 in 1959 and a year later they hit No. 1 with another original, 'Shakin' All Over' (written hurriedly in Chas McDevitt's Freight Train coffee bar, and intended as only a throwaway B-side), a song which in 1965 would give Canadian group Guess Who their first US hit. Ex-Covent Garden fruit and vegetable market worker Tommy Bruce was another performer who seemed to have his roots firmly planted in mid-1950s r'n'r. His voice, which sounded like he gargled with gravel, was described by the media as 'the most unique in Tin Pan Alley for a decade' and by himself as 'diabolical'. This unmistakable vocalist had a one-off left-field hit in 1960 with his tongue-in-cheek interpretation of Fats Waller's old favourite 'Ain't Misbehavin'', which he and his aptly named group the Bruisers took to the Top 3.

Among the best of the other rootsy rock-oriented artists who first recorded between 1958 and 1962 were Vince Taylor & The Playboys, Cliff Bennett & The Rebel Rousers, Dicky Pride, Wee Willie Harris, Vince Eager, Screaming Lord Sutch, Roy Young and Howie Casey & The Seniors.

As the fabulous Fifties ended, Cliff Richard and the Shadows were the most influential and imitated act in the land. Where they ventured musically, others were sure to follow. Richard, as mentioned earlier, was already evolving from a raunchy rock'n'roller to a clean-cut pop star, and the Shadows would soon be starting a record-breaking run of instrumental hits.

Tommy Bruce samples the low-fi in a bit of the latest high-tech

TOMMY STEELE

Born Thomas Hicks in London, this singer/songwriter/entertainer was the first genuine British rock'n'roller. He was in the merchant navy in 1952-6, during which time he developed a love of American country music through the recordings of Hank Williams (Steele recorded three of his songs on his debut album), Red Foley and Tennessee Ernie Ford, and while on shore leave he would play guitar in the C&W band, Jack Fallon & The Sons Of The Saddle. Thanks to regular US trips, he was one of the first Britons to see Elvis Presley perform, and this possibly influenced his stage act when he appeared at London's 2 I's coffee bar. It was here that he was spotted by John Kennedy, who realised that this chirpy cockney with the mop of bouncy blonde hair could become Britain's first home-grown rock'n'roll star. George Martin at Parlophone did not see Steele's potential, however, but Decca Records did: the exact opposite would happen with The Beatles six years later. Steele wrote his first single, 'Rock With The Cavemen', with friends Mike Pratt and Lionel Bart (who later penned such successful works as Cliff Richard's 'Living Doll' and the musical *Oliver*), and he was backed on the record by a team of UK jazz musicians, including poll-winning saxophonist Ronnie Scott. An early Steele review said 'he lacks the essential authentic flavour' but this certainly did not deter Kennedy and his partner, Larry Parnes, from assembling an ingenious marketing plan for the 19-year-old. After a short residency at London's prestigious Stork Club he landed a coveted spot on Jack Payne's top-rated TV show *Off The Record* on October 15th, 1956. Reviewers noted his 'untidy hair' but this type of comment helped the single's progress, and a week later he had his first hit on his hands. Almost instantly, he was hailed by the media as 'Britain's answer to Elvis', was headlining a tour and being greeted with hysteria on a scale likened to that for Johnnie Ray. In 1957 Steele's career as a rocker reached its pinnacle. In January he successfully appeared at London's swanky niterie, the Café Paris, and his third release, 'Singing The Blues', topped the chart (a feat even Elvis had not yet accomplished). Also that year, *The Tommy Steele Story* was a hit film and album, and he had a further five chart singles, including his compositions, 'Butterfingers', 'Water Water' and 'Handful Of Songs'. The 1957 *NME* polls also showed how highly UK record buyers regarded him. He won the award for British Music Personality, and came second to Elvis Presley in the World Music Personality category. To top off a breathtaking twelve months, he appeared in the Royal Variety Performance, and was the subject of an hour-long BBC TV special. In the following year he became the first rocker to have his wax likeness in Madame Tussaud's and the first to be the subject of TV's *This Is Your Life*. The press called him 'a sensational discovery for pantomime' after his appearance in 'Goldilocks', and reviewers of his second major film, *The Duke Wore Jeans*, admitted he was 'more than just a rock and roller.' Like all British record stars before him, Steele's aim was to be an all-round entertainer and his dream was to star in a Hollywood musical. He proved he was talented enough to achieve both these goals and more. Incidentally, his 1958 hit 'Nairobi', was penned by Bob Merrill, composer of the stage musical *Some Like It Hot*, in which Steele successfully starred in 1992.

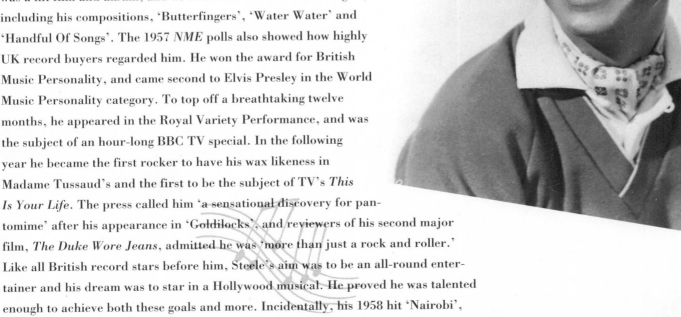

Tousle-headed Tommy Steeele as he appeared in the quickest bio-pic in rock'n'roll movie history, *The Tommy Steele Story*, which was filmed and released in 1957 less than a year after his debut

TERRY DENE

A London-born singer who was discovered at Soho's famous 2 I's coffee bar, Terry Dene's big break came when he appeared on *6.5 Special* in April 1957. After being rejected by Columbia, he was signed by Decca and had three Top 20 hits in1957-8: 'A White Sports Coat', 'Stairway Of Love' and 'Start Movin''. The first two songs had originally been recorded by Marty Robbins, and the third by singer/actor/drummer Sal Mineo. Fame brought many problems to the singer who was tagged 'Britain's Elvis'. In 1958, this one- time screen extra starred in the unsuccessful British pop film, *The Golden Disc*, and was fined both for drunkenness and vandalism. Dene, who had a history of mental disturbance, was inducted into the army with the full press treatment in 1959. A battalion of media men were also present when he was released as 'medically unfit' just two months later. The end of his short marriage to singer Edna Savage continued to earn him the kind of publicity that curtailed his career prematurely. After abandoning pop music, Dene became a street singing evangelist and recorded some religious material. In the 1980s he returned to live rock, backed by members of his original Dene-Aces. Dene, whose live performances were always more exciting than his records, was welcomed back by many UK rock'n'roll fans like a long-lost brother.

Terry Dene (above)
giving it all he's got

Russ Hamilton (right)
had a surprise million-
seller on his hands with
'We Will Make Love', a
1957 hit on both sides
of the Atlantic

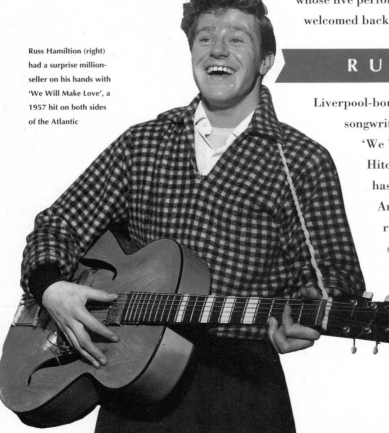

RUSS HAMILTON

Liverpool-born Russ Hamilton (real name Ronald Hulme) was a singer/ songwriter who had an amazing start to his career. His first single 'We Will Make Love' (written for an ex-girlfriend, Pat Hitchin), narrowly missed the top of the UK chart, and the hastily written B-side, 'Rainbow' sold over a million copies in America, becoming the first record by a Merseyside act to reach the US Top 10. This success meant that Hamilton spent the summer of 1957 commuting between the USA and Clacton where he was entertaining children as a Redcoat at a Butlins holiday camp. In the annual *Billboard* disc jockey poll he was voted second Most Promising New Male Singer in America (Johnny Mathis was first and Paul Anka third). His follow up, 'Wedding

Ring', again written about Miss Hitchin, was a minor UK hit but failed to ignite much interest Stateside. In 1960 he joined MGM Records who flew him to Nashville to record. However, there was to be no more gold at the end of the rainbow for the likeable Merseyside minstrel who had sent America an early warning that 'The Redcoats Are Coming!'.

Despite the sheet music plug for the record, 'I Got A Robe' failed to clothe Laurie London with a follow-up hit, and now he's in the rag trade proper

LAURIE LONDON

This confident 13-year-old Londoner walked on to the BBC stand at the 1957 Earls Court Radio Show and told them they should let him sing. He borrowed Malcolm Mitchell's guitar and burst into 'The Ballad Of Jesse James'. He so impressed everyone present that he soon found himself in EMI's recording studios with producer Norman Newell, and appearing on *6.5 Special*. His first single, a hand-clapping version of the old Negro spiritual, 'He's Got The Whole World (In His Hands)', coupled with 'Cradle Rock', narrowly missed the UK Top 10, and when released in America in early 1958 shot to the top of the 'Cash Box' chart, selling well over a million copies. American DJs voted him the third Most Promising New Singer of 1958, right behind hit machines Jimmie Rodgers and Johnny Mathis. It seemed the London schoolboy had the whole world in his hands, but he never found the winning formula again, and after a dozen unsuccessful singles he quit the business. He is now a well-known figure in the clothing industry.

An in-action shot of Jim Dale by Fifties photographer of the stars Harry Hammond

JIM DALE

Before trying his hand professionally at singing, Northamptonshire-born Dale (real name James Smith) had 'trod the boards' extensively as an impressionist, part of a comedy tumbling act and a solo comedian. He joined BBC TV's *6.5 Special* in April 1957, and shortly afterwards he was signed to the Parlophone label, where he was produced by house A&R man George Martin. His only Top 20 hit came with his second single, 'Be My Girl', which reached No. 2. He had three more British Top 40 entries, the last of them coming in 1958 with a version of the McGuire Sisters' American hit 'Sugartime' (the original, recorded by composer Charlie Phillips, had featured Buddy Holly on guitar and Cricket Jerry Allison on drums). In the Sixties he appeared in a string of the highly successful *Carry On comedy* films and he also co-wrote the 1967 Seekers' smash 'Georgy Girl'. Dale relocated to the US and starred in several notable films including *Digby* in 1973 and the hit Broadway musical *Pete's Dragon* in 1979. The amiable actor and singer was also one of the stars of the 1992 film *Carry On Columbus*.

When Vince Taylor's 'Brand New Cadillac' was re-released in the late Seventies, it was a cult hit with a new generation of jivers

VINCE TAYLOR & THE PLAYBOYS

Many people thought that Vince Taylor (born Brian Holden) was American, and he would have been the last person to deny it. He was actually born in West London and moved to California in 1954 when he was 17. His master plan was to return to the UK as a visiting American rocker, form a rock'n'roll band, and become a top star – and, as they say, two out of three ain't bad. In early 1958 he returned and formed the first of several line-ups of The Playboys, which initially included such noteworthies as Tony Sheridan (whom The Beatles later backed on record), Brian 'Liquorice' Locking and Brian Bennett (who both went on to join the Shadows). The group, who aimed to look like clones of Gene Vincent & The Blue Caps, were spotted at the 2 I's, which led to their appearing on *Oh Boy!*, and signing with Parlophone. Their first release, which coupled two Sun Records originals, 'Right Behind You Baby' (first recorded by Ray Smith) and 'I Like Love' (earlier cut by Roy Orbison), was overlooked by record buyers. The follow-up, 'Brand New Cadillac' (later recorded by The Clash), was a near miss in 1959, and a year later, their debut single on Palette, 'Jet Black Machine', parked itself in some UK charts. Taylor was a good stage performer but was always regarded as a second Gene Vincent – a description he hated but one he seemed to go out of his way to earn. Taylor, who finally found success when he relocated to France in the 1960s, died in 1991.

Marty Wilde marrying 18-year-old Joyce Baker, one of the Vernons Girls, at Christ Church, Trafalgar Road, Greenwich, in December 1959

MARTY WILDE

Londoner Marty Wilde (born Reginald Smith) sang with South London skiffle group the Hound Dogs before making his solo club debut at London's Blue Angel in July 1957. He was discovered shortly afterwards by Larry Parnes while appearing at the Condor Club (under the name Reg Patterson) above the Sabrina coffee bar in London's West End. Parnes saw a lot of potential in the very tall, dark-haired, photogenic singer/guitarist. He was quickly added to a Parnes package show and was an instant success with the scream-agers. Wilde's debut single coupled Jimmie Rodgers' US hit 'Honeycomb' (with revised lyrics to escape a BBC ban), and a Wilde original, 'Wild Cat'. Although neither this single nor his versions of Jimmy Edwards' 'Love Bug Crawl' or Jimmie Rodgers' 'Oh Oh I'm Falling In Love Again' charted, Wilde and his excellent backing group The Wildcats (who included Big Jim Sullivan, Brian Bennett and Brian 'Liquorice' Locking) were building up a massive following via live shows and numerous TV appearances. His first hit came in the summer of 1958, with the suicide saga 'Endless Sleep', produced, as were most of his hits, by Johnny Franz. Wilde joined the regulars on TV's *Oh Boy!* and in 1959, hosted Jack Good's new television show *Boy Meets Girls*, as well as appearing on a Royal Variety Show. After a couple of less successful releases he strung together a run of four successive Top 10 singles, 'Donna' (a Ritchie Valens song), 'A Teenager In Love', which outsold not only the Dion & The Belmonts original version but a UK cover by Craig Douglas, 'Sea Of Love', which had earlier been recorded by R&B singer Phil Phillips, and the self-composed 'Bad Boy'. In early 1960 the latter single also shot into the US Top 50 (despite several American cover versions), and the recently married Wilde took his honeymoon in the States, so that he could promote it. While in New York he recorded 10 tracks for the American market (in a day!) with Chuck Sagle (who had previously arranged hits for Bobby Darin and Connie Francis). None of them charted Stateside, but 'Little Girl' (released at the time of his daughter Kim's birth) and a riveting revival of 'Angry' added to his British hit tally. However, the fact that they were not the giant hits people had come to expect from him encouraged some critics to start writing him off. They blamed either his marriage (which was considered the kiss of death to a teen idol) or his over-exposure on TV for his failure to reach the Top 10. However, in early 1961 he bounced back again like a 'Rubber Ball', which coincidentally was the title of his next Top 10 hit. Wilde then branched out into films and musicals, starring in the South African-made movie *The Hellions* in 1961 and in the West End production of *Bye Bye Birdie*. After another less successful sales period, he took Frankie Laine's 1951 hit 'Jezebel', added a 'Raunchy'-like theme to it, and found himself back in the Top 30. Although his hits stopped about the time The Beatles arrived on the scene, the singer, who had even had a teen magazine (*Marty*) named after him, continued to perform in various guises for several years, returning to the US chart with 'Abergavenny' in 1969 (under the name Shannon). He also later wrote hits for Status Quo ('Ice In The Sun'), Lulu ('I'm A Tiger') and The Casuals('Jesamine') as well as co-writing and producing many successful records for his 'little girl' Kim.

Marty Wilde – along with Cliff and Billy Fury he was one of the Big Three (and certainly the tallest) of British rock'n'roll in the late Fifties

CLIFF RICHARD

The most successful British solo singer of all time was born Harry Webb in Lucknow, India (his father's job in the wine business necessitated spending many

The US Top Five version of 'Endless Sleep' by Jody Reynolds started a whole spate of 'death discs' in the late Fifties

Who would have thought he'd become the eternal boy-next-door, the Mr Clean of British pop, when Cliff Richard's scowling bump-and-grind was launched on an unsuspecting public

years overseas). School friends in Hertfordshire best remember him for being the Cheshunt Secondary Modern's javelin throwing champion and for being in a vocal quintet, aptly named the Quintones. In 1957 he joined a skiffle combo at the Trinity Youth Club in Waltham Cross, Essex, which led to his becoming a member of the Dick Teague Skiffle Group. In 1958, together with drummer Terry Smart and guitarist Norman Mitham, he formed Harry Webb & The Drifters and recorded a demo of Jerry Lee Lewis' 'Breathless' and Lloyd Price's 'Lawdy Miss Clawdy'. The group were soon booked into the (even then) legendary 2 I's coffee bar, and shortly afterwards guitarist/ songwriter Ian 'Sammy' Samwell joined their ranks. Things then moved quickly for the 17-year-old singer. He was renamed Cliff Richard and his demo found its way to Columbia Records. Producer Norrie Paramor said 'I receive hundreds of demos and most fail to create any sort of impact. However, when I heard Cliff, I really sat up and took notice.' His debut single 'Move It' (which featured guitar work from noted session men Frank Clarke and Ernie Shears) reached No. 2 in October 1958, and his live performances were greeted by a fan fervour that surpassed even that for Tommy Steele at his peak. Before the year ended, he returned to the Top 10 with another Samwell composed rocker, 'High Class Baby', and had been voted Britain's Favourite New Singer in the prestigious *NME* poll. In 1959 he made his film debut in *Serious Charge*, which was quickly followed by the leading role in the musical *Expresso Bongo* (pipping Marty Wilde at the post for this part), and that year's hits included two No. 1s, 'Living Doll' and 'Travellin' Light'. By the time The Beatles debuted on the chart, Richard had amassed 22 Top 20 entries, the vast majority of which were not cover versions, unlike the releases of many of his rivals. However, like the Liverpool lads, Richard's first two albums contained many carefully chosen covers of American songs. His popularity did not slide during the swinging sixties, nor did his star glitter any less during the glam rock days, and the adoration his fans felt for him outlived the punk craze that followed it. During the 1980s he accumulated more UK Top 10 albums than any other act, and in the 1990s is still a permanent fixture in the charts. Richard has charted with over 100 singles, has won innumerable awards (including an OBE) over the years and broken countless records, including the one Elvis Presley held for so long for the most Top 10 hits in Britain. He is simply without parallel in British pop music history.

LORD ROCKINGHAM'S XI

TV producer Jack Good decided that the resident backing band on his show *Oh Boy!* should sound as distinctive as their name (the original Lord Rockingham being a past English politician). Not being musical, he gave noted arranger Harry Robinson the brief to find a unique sound and provided him with a large pile of recent good and bad US r'n'r records to study, convinced that somewhere between the two extremes lay the answer. Good suggested that organist Cherry Wainer be an integral part of the outfit, and Robinson teamed her with a number of top UK musicians (the 13-piece band at times included Red Price and music critic Benny Green) as he was convinced that 'You've got to have the best in order to produce amusing and unorthodox sounds.' Robinson admitted 'It all started as a gigantic joke and we always had tremendous fun at the recording studios.' Their first release, 'Fried Onions', was a standout rock instrumental, which featured vocal interjections by Good, who said, 'It had everything on it but the kitchen sink.' It entered the US Top 100 in 1958, indicating that they were doing something right. The follow-up 'Hoots Mon', which was composed by Robinson, was a Scottish relation of 'Tequila'. It topped the British chart, and the similar Celtic novelty, 'Wee Tom', gave them their second Top 20 entry. The zestful band's lack of further hits may have been due to the legal problems that followed between Good and Robinson over the band's future – the outcome being that the rights to the group's name belonged to Good for recording and TV, and to Robinson for live work.

Just to remind us that pop could be as inane as its critics claimed, Jackie Dennis graced the charts for a few brief months during 1958

JACKIE DENNIS

This Edinburgh-born singer was spotted by comedians Mike and Bernie Winters performing at an American Air Force base. They brought him to the attention of top agent/manager Eve Taylor, who booked him on *6.5 Special*, where his impact was immediate – he was quickly added to the cast of the *6.5 Special* film, and it was even announced that he was to start filming *The Jackie Dennis Story*. The future looked very bright indeed in 1958 for the kilt-clad 15-year-old pop singer, whose first single, 'La Dee Dah', had soared into the UK Top 20 Best Sellers just two weeks after release. Television and live bookings flooded in and he flew to the US to appear in Perry Como's top-rated TV show where he was introduced as 'Britain's Ricky

Nelson'. Despite all this ballyhoo, record buyers failed to purchase his future releases in any significant quantity, and he was soon a teen has-been. He is now reported to be driving a bus in Edinburgh.

Lord Rockingham tenor sax player Benny Green was said to always wear dark glasses on *Oh Boy!* so he wouldn't be recognised by his fellow jazz musicians

BILLY FURY

No Liverpool act (The Beatles included) has achieved as many British chart entries as Billy Fury (born Ronald Wycherley), who ranked alongside Cliff Richard and Marty Wilde as the three most popular British rockers at the start of the 1960s. In 1958, when he was only 17, Fury sent a demo of six recordings to impresario Larry Parnes, who invited him backstage at the Birkenhead Essoldo to play some of his songs to Marty Wilde. Wilde and Parnes were duly impressed, both with the commercial possibilities of his compositions, and with Fury's striking Elvis-like good looks. The story goes that Parnes (who gave Wycherley his stage name) insisted the young unknown go on stage that very night and perform as part of the package show, and, as happens in the best Hollywood bio-pics, he was a huge success. After Wilde's label, Philips, had rejected Fury, he signed with Decca, making his TV debut on *Cool For Cats* in February 1959. He quickly became a top attraction on *Oh Boy!*, caused pandemonium wherever he played, and soon accumulated a few self-composed hits. His Presley-esque stage performance, which was labelled 'offensive' by many critics, naturally made him a 'must' for pop TV shows, and in 1960 he became a regular on *Boy Meets Girls*, and was the star of *Wham!* Also during that year, Fury released the totally self-composed album The Sound Of Fury, which with hindsight many regard as the finest rockabilly album produced in Britain. Soon afterwards, Fury resorted to covering American songs, with the emphasis on dramatic beat ballads, a genre in which he excelled. Among his biggest hits of this period were versions of Tony Orlando's 'Halfway To Heaven' and 'I'd Never Find Another You', the Rivileers' 'A Thousand Stars' and a clever arrangement of 'Jealousy', a song which had been originally popularised in 1951 by Frankie Laine. Unlike most early British rock acts Fury survived the initial onslaught of Merseybeat, and thanks to a well-chosen mixture of US and

Billy Fury's 'Halfway To Paradise' is now considered by many to be one of the all-time classics of pop ballad singing

British songs actually added a further nine Top 20 hits to his tally in 1963-5. During his career Fury also starred in three films, *Play It Cool* in 1962, the equally forgettable *I've Gotta Horse* in 1965, with his best-known role being that of rock singer Stormy Tempest in David Essex's 1973 hit movie, *That'll Be The Day*. Fury, who had always suffered with poor health, and knew that he was destined to have only a short life, died of heart failure in 1983 aged 42.

TOMMY BRUCE

Tommy Bruce played his tough-guy working bloke image for all it was worth

Tommy Bruce was an Eastender whose voice was described as 'a subtle blending of a corncrake, steam hammer and gravel polisher.' Orphaned at the age of 10, he worked for several years as a truck driver's mate in London's famous Covent Garden vegetable market. In 1960, his neighbour Barry Mason (later a successful songwriter) encouraged him to make the demo that got him a record deal. Many would have rejected Bruce out of hand, but Columbia Records' Norrie Paramor felt 'he might click with the youngsters.' His debut single 'Ain't Misbehavin'', which narrowly missed the top spot in 1960, was his only major hit, although he also charted with the follow up, 'Broken Doll', and, briefly, in 1962 with 'Babette'. Bruce was accused of sounding like the Big Bopper (his biggest hit opened 'Hello doll', much as the Big Bopper's 'Chantilly Lace' had started with a similarly voiced 'Hello baby'). He hotly disputed this claim, saying 'I really didn't know the late singer's work that well.' Although he possessed limited musical talent, his larger than life personality and unique vocal technique helped to enliven and amplify the humour in the UK rock scene.

ROY YOUNG

Roy Young was one of the most authentic and, arguably, the wildest of the early UK rockers. He may have been a Little Richard clone, but he was an excellent one, and deserves to be regarded as one of Britain's foremost rock'n'roll performers of that era. The near-manic singer/pianist's many appearances on the TV shows *Drumbeat* and *Oh Boy!* in 1959-60 gave the staid British music scene a much needed shake up, and was a refreshing reminder of how untamed and exciting rock could be. Young released several outstanding singles, including explosive interpretations of Sonny Spencer's 'Gilee' and Dee Clark's US hits 'Just Keep It Up' and 'Hey Little Girl'. An early 1970s comeback attracted the kind of media interest he could have used ten years earlier, but it did not push the *Mr. Funk* album by the Roy Young Band (which also included Howie Casey) into the chart.

The Pirates, led by guitarist Mick Green, enjoyed a second lease of life on the London pub rock scene in the Seventies

Johnny Kidd and The Pirates bridged the gap between Fifties rock'n'roll and Sixties beat music with a string of hits topped by the chart-topping 'Shakin' All Over'

HOWIE CASEY & THE SENIORS

The Seniors, one of the first and best beat groups on Merseyside, were formed by saxophonist Howie Casey after he left the services. As Derry & The Seniors they became the first beat group booked into the Hamburg clubs (Casey criticised his agent, Allan Williams, for then sending over 'a bum group like The Beatles.') In 1962 they had a residency at the Inn At The Top club, in Ilford, East London, and recorded an album, Twist At The Top, featuring vocalists Derry Wilkie and Freddie Fowell (later known as comedian Freddie Starr). Their single, 'Double Twist', really rocked but was too frenzied for the new dance: 'We play everything at 100 miles an hour, and try to blind people with our speed rather than technique', Casey confessed. When their much deserved success was not forthcoming the group split, and Casey made several standout records as part of Kingsize Taylor & The Dominoes, before joining the Roy Young band. Since the late 1960s Casey has mainly been active as a session man, although he toured with Wings and played on their classic Band On The Run album.

JOHNNY KIDD & THE PIRATES

Johnny Kidd (born Frederick Heath in London) and his backing group The Pirates are rightly regarded as one of the most important British rock acts of the pre-Beatles era. After leaving The Five Nutters skiffle group, Kidd and fellow Nutter Alan Caddy (later of The Tornados) formed the first of many line-ups of The Pirates. Their debut disc in 1959 was 'Please Don't Touch', written by the then 18-year-old Kidd. It was a cut above most UK-originated rock songs of the time, was covered in America, and deserved more than its lowly Top 30 placing. Their biggest hit came in 1960 with Kidd's self-composed 'Shakin' All Over', which reached No. 1 on some charts. This was followed into the chart by another original, 'Restless'. Kidd was modest about his song-writing abilities, saying 'I don't consider "Shakin' All Over" to be a real song - there's nothing worthwhile musically in it.' In 1961 the pirate-garbed group and their eyepatch-wearing lead singer (it hid a bad cast in his eye) resorted to covering US rock and R&B songs, generally with disappointing results. At the height of the Merseybeat craze they scored two final Top 30 entries, 'I'll Never Get Over You' and 'Hungry For Love', both written by ex-Viscount Gordon Mills (who later managed Tom Jones, Engelbert Humperdinck and Gilbert O'Sullivan). Although American success eluded the group, they are considered by US critics to be pivotal figures in the British rock scene. *Rolling Stone* said 'They were a prototype for the heavy-metal guitar trios that they predated by nearly a decade.' Kidd, who was arguably Britain's most commercial rock writer before The Beatles, died in a car crash in 1966.

Pride before a fall – Dickie's was one of the tragic stories of British rock'n'roll

DICKIE PRIDE

This ultra-energetic, London-born rock'n'roller (real name Richard Knellar) may have been one of the least successful members of manager Larry Parnes' stable of British rock artists in the early 1960s, but he was regarded by many critics, and several of his stablemates, as the most talented. Chart-topping pianist Russ Conway brought him to the attention of both Columbia Records' A&R head Norrie Paramor and Parnes, persuading them to see Pride perform at a South London pub. Paramor signed him, Parnes snapped him up and quickly put him in one of his package shows, and Jack Good (who called Pride 'one of the most talented young singers in the country') gave him a regular spot on *Oh Boy!* Pride, tagged 'the sheik of shake' because of the semi-epileptic fits he often feigned whilst singing on stage, had his biggest hit in 1959 with 'Primrose Lane', a cover of Jerry Wallace's ballad, which strolled into the Top 30. However, he is probably best remembered for his version of Little Richard's 'Slippin' And Slidin', Barry DeVorzon's 'Betty Betty' and 'Frantic'. The tireless entertainer, whose album Pride Without Prejudice, recorded with Ted Heath's Orchestra, contained only MOR and jazz standards, died of drug-related causes, aged 27, in 1969. When news of his death reached Parnes he said 'When talent like this is wasted it's a crying shame. This boy could have been a big, big star - everybody said it.'

Cliff Bennett and the boys came out of the era of the Hit Parade Heroes to make it big in the Beat Boom that followed

CLIFF BENNETT & THE REBEL ROUSERS

Slough-born Cliff Bennett, who named his backing group after a Duane Eddy hit, started his recording career under the guidance of noted producer/songwriter Joe Meek. His first release in 1961 on Parlophone was a double A-side, coupling a cover of Jerry Lee Lewis' 'When I Get Paid' with a Meek original 'That's What I Said'. This underrated single was one of the best r'n'r records ever recorded in Britain. It had a genuine American feel, and both sides rocked like there was no tomorrow. His follow up, 'You Got What I Like', was also an outstanding example of British rock'n'roll, and the fact that neither single garnered much airplay and very few sales was less a reflection on their content, than an indication of how soft rock had become by 1961. Bennett's records had all the energy and excitement of the early rock greats, but this sheer exuberance had by then become a hindrance. In 1962, the group followed in the footsteps of The Beatles and other unwanted British rockers and went to Hamburg, where real rootsy music was still appreciated. Bennett, who without doubt had one of the strongest voices in British pop, scored his biggest hits with versions of The Drifters 'One Way Love' in 1964 and his cover of an album track by fellow retro- rockers, The Beatles, 'Got To Get You Into My Life', in 1966.

CUDDLY DUDLEY

Thanks to numerous appearances on TVs *Oh Boy!* and his many warmly received live appearances, Cuddly Dudley (real name Dudley Heslop) was probably the best known British-based black rock'n'roll artist in the late 1950s. He joined HMV records in 1959, and released two unsuccessful singles on the label 'Lots More Love', and a cover version of Chuck Berry's 'Too Pooped To Pop' in 1960. Dudley, who toured the UK supporting The Platters in 1960, moved to Ember records in 1961, but the track 'Sitting In A Train' also failed to steam up the chart. His highly regarded backing group, The Redcaps, consisted of Frank Farley (drums), Johnny Spence (bass), Johnny Patto (guitar) and Mick Green (guitar), who later became Johnny Kidd's group The Pirates.

Cuddly Dudley (right), possibly ahead of his time, might have fared better had he been part of the early Sixties R&B movement rather than the rock'n'roll scene that preceded it

Espresso Bongo

THE COFFEE BAR CULT

In the 1950s most youngsters were still living at home and, as can be imagined, many were desperate to get out for at least for an evening or two a week. Before the mid-1950s there were few meeting places for teenagers apart from youth clubs, which were often held in draughty old church halls, or in the function room above the local Co-op (Co-operative store). At these clubs they were supervised by vicars or parents, and in exchange for the membership fee (usually about 2s 6d [13p] a term), teenagers would get little more than a cup of tea, a biscuit (which was sometimes extra), a game of table tennis and a chance to chat indoors with their mates.

To help add a little excitement to the lives of these young people and to help relieve them of any excess money in their pockets, coffee bars sprouted up right across Britain, and these soon became the social centre for many teenagers. The focal point was often the bulky coin-operated American juke boxes. Mighty Wurlitzers, rockin' Rock-Olas or bass heavy Bel Ami's offered customers up to 100 titles; the pick of 50 10-inch 78rpm records clipped to a rotating metal wheel would be delivered to the turntable. The cost was sixpence for one play or a shilling (5p) for three, and watching the process was as entertaining, and often as loud, as hearing the record. No coffee bar would be complete without a space-age Italian coffee machine (preferably made by Gaggia), which would noisily splutter out espresso and cappuccino coffee, each cup of frothy coffee costing about nine pence (4p).

It seemed that by the end of the decade every high street had its own coffee bar

The spartan interior of the local youth club, like this one in Sheffield, was the nearest younger teenagers got to the exotic atmosphere of a proper dancehall

The advent of the coffee bar with Italian espresso machines and 'Scandinavian' pine furniture brought a rare 'continental' atmosphere to High Streets all over Great Britain

where teenagers met to dance (if it was possible) and chat, with conversation ranging from normal teen-talk to deep discussions about the world's problems. The most famous of all the thousands of them was undoubtedly the 2 I's at 57 Old Compton Street, Soho, in the heart of London's West End, which was owned by Paul Lincoln (who also worked as the wrestler Dr. Death). Songwriter Lionel Bart recalled, 'All the kids had at the 2 I's was cappuccino, Coca-Cola, a jukebox and a basement' - but what a basement! It was in that small cellar that many of the top British stars of 1957-61 got their first break, including Tommy Steele, Cliff Richard, Adam Faith and Terry Dene (whom Lincoln managed). At any given time, you would find about 150 teenagers crammed into the basement, rubbing shoulders with record label A&R men who had come looking for likely new talent. Incidentally, Lincoln charged cellar customers a shilling admission after he realised that many of them had developed the knack of making each coffee last an hour or more.

Wally Whyton, who played there as part of The Vipers skiffle group, said, 'The 2 I's was remarkably small. Upstairs you could get ten people sitting along the front of the counter. Downstairs, it was a long narrow room, 12 feet wide and 20 feet long. It was run like a variety theatre (we sometimes had two houses) where we sang from 7 'till 9, and then from 9.30 'till 11.30. People would queue round the block to see us.' The 2 I's became so famous that skifflers and would-be r'n'r stars from every corner of Britain made a pilgrimage to Soho in the hope that Old Compton Street would be paved with gold records for them. It became such an important part of the UK music scene that records were even

The forerunners to coffee bars were a post-war chain called National Milk Bars serving milk shakes and ice cream sundaes American-style

made about it, including 'Rockin' At The Two I's' by Wee Willie Harris and 'Two Eyes' by Tommy Steele. This compact coffee bar, where, some say, the Hand Jive was born, was the venue of the first outside broadcast of *6.5 Special* in November 1957. It was also there, in 1960, that Bruno Koschmider came looking for groups to play in his Hamburg club and by chance met Allan Williams, owner of a Merseyside coffee bar, the Jacaranda. Williams recommended Liverpool groups, and the rest is history. Apart from the 2 I's (which is now the Italian restaurant, 'Le Bistingo'), the West End's best-known coffee bars were probably Heaven & Hell, which was next door to the 2 I's, Chas McDevitt's Freight Train in Berwick Street, The Skiffle Cellar in Greek Street, The Breadbasket in Cleveland Street and Le Macabre (where customers sat on coffins) in Meard Street.

Youth clubs and coffee bars were so much a part of 1950s British teenager's lifestyle that UK pop films of the era were often centred around them. Youth Clubs were featured in such films as *Serious Charge*, *Some People* and *The Young Ones* and coffee bars were shown as the launching pad for hit singers in movies like *The Tommy Steele Story*, *The Golden Disc* and *Expresso Bongo*. Even four decades later in 1993 the successful Carlton-TV series, *Head Over Heels*, which was set in the 1950s, heavily featured a coffee bar and coffee-bar singers.

The Heaven and Hell (above) was one of the best-known coffee bars in London's Soho, as of course was the now-legendary 2 I's where (below) Vince Taylor, among many other rock stars, hung out

If You Can't Beat 'em

The Crooners Cash In

Once rock'n'roll had got its blue suede shoe-shod foot in the door of British popular music, it quickly forced it wide open, sending shock waves throughout the entertainment industry. In the late 1950s the number of record buyers increased as drastically as their average age decreased. Suddenly singers and bands, who only months before had been chart regulars, were considered 'square' by these new youthful consumers and suffered plummeting sales.

Although they were earning good money from rock, many record companies and music publishers still hoped for a return to the days of 'good music'. As producer George Martin noted, 'Gimmick value had taken precedence over artistry, and sometimes I think that in this country the accompaniments are too good for the artists.'

Casualties of the first wave of rock'n'roll included big-voiced balladeer Lee Lawrence who left for America, Australian Jimmy Parkinson (he had a UK hit with the Platters' 'The Great Pretender') who returned home; hit songstress Suzi Miller relocated to Germany, top A&R man Ray Martin resigned from Columbia Records and Cyril Stapleton pulled the curtain down on his show band after five very successful years.

In America at this time many parents, politicians and preachers felt that the answer was to ban r'n'r. However, this not only strengthened the resolve of the rock flock but attracted many more teenagers into the fold, much in the way that 'parental advisory' stickers on rap albums do nowadays.

Teenagers were not about to melt down their Presley platters and stock up on Sinatra, and any music industry person failing to absorb this fact could find themselves out in the cold.

In Britain, many more pre-rock performers followed the precept 'if you can't beat them, join them', and added a back beat to their ballads and a rock rhythm (albeit often slight) to their up tempo recordings. Like the majority of mid-1950s British attempts at rock, many of these later records also proved to be commercial disasters. Few people rushed out to buy the Beverley Sisters' version of the Everly Brothers' 'Bye Bye Love', Lita Roza's cover of Ruth Brown's 'Lucky Lips' or Billie Anthony's interpretation of Guy Mitchell's hit, 'Rock-A-Billy'.

Instrumentals like Ronnie Aldrich's 'Rock & Roll Boogie', ' Rock Mr. Piper' by Desmond Lane, Cyril Stapleton's 'Rock Fiddle Rock' or jazz poll winners The Kirchins' 'Rock Around The World' also met lukewarm responses.

In 1957 Ruby Murray belted out the Bobby Charles/Bill Haley rock anthem 'See You Later Alligator' on TV and Dickie Valentine incorporated an Elvis impersonation into his act in order to keep up with the fast-changing times. There were, however, pre-rock favourites who not only survived but thrived when they added more beat (with a small b) to their backing tracks. Michael Holliday collected a couple of chart toppers, Gary Miller and Tony Brent held their own for a while and Frankie Vaughan went from strength to strength. Vaughan, who had been recording since 1950, with scant success, scored in 1955 with covers of 'Tweedle Dee' (originally by LaVern Baker) and 'Seventeen', and a year later with 'My Boy Flat Top' (the last two previously recorded by Boyd Bennett & His Rockets) and 'Green Door' (Jim Lowe's US hit) which narrowly missed the top spot. By cleverly combining a mixture of beat and ballads Vaughan stayed at the forefront of the British pop scene until the mid-1960s.

These MOR merchants helped smooth rock's rough edges, soften its sound, and turn it into a more palatable product that appealed not only to the less discerning British teenager (and there have always been more of these than one would imagine), but also to many of the older generation. Raw rock, which had already been diluted to broaden its appeal, was now being further watered down and dissolved into the general mill pool of pop.

Appropriately named, Dickie Valentine had the fans screaming right through the Fifties, and a string of hits that included two Number Ones, 'Finger Of Suspicion' in 1954 and 1955's seasonal smash 'Christmas Alphabet'

FRANKIE VAUGHAN

This larger-than-life big voiced pop/cabaret star was born Frank Abelson in Liverpool. His first recording was a cover version of the Mills Brothers' US hit 'Daddy's Little Girl' in 1950 on Decca. He joined HMV in 1952, and first charted two years later with a novelty song 'Istanbul'. In 1955, the top hat-wearing, cane-carrying, high-kicking, Victor Mature look-alike signed to Philips, and 'Tweedle Dee' in 1955 gave him the first of his 22 Top 40 hits for the label. Vaughan reached the top of his trade in the UK, headlined bills all over Britain and starred in several films, before turning his attention to the US. American television impressario Ed Sullivan called him 'sensational' and the leading US record producer of the time,

Like Valentine, Lita Roza (opposite) graduated through the Ted Heath band to become a solo star in her own right. Her all-woman image went down well with the males in the audience, though her biggest record hit was the twee '53 chart-topper 'How Much Is That Doggie In The Window?'

Mitch Miller, said ' He has everything it takes - and not in small doses either.' His record of 'Judy' in 1958 reached the American chart. However, despite recording several singles especially for the US market, this was to be a feat he would not repeat. In 1959 he became the first British artist to headline at New York's prestigious Copacabana club, and soon afterwards was filming in Hollywood with Marilyn Monroe. In Britain his rock-related hits included covers of 'Seventeen', 'My Boy Flat Top', 'Green Door', Charlie Gracie's 'Wanderin' Eyes' and the chart-topping 'Tower Of Strength', which Gene McDaniels had taken into the US Top 5. However, Vaughan always seemed more at home with mainstream cabaret songs like his 1918-composed signature tune 'Give Me The Moonlight' which helped make him – and his top hat and cane – something of an institution in British show business.

Frankie Vaughan (above) affected the stage-door-Johnny image of another era, while Gary Miller made a gimmick of his casual appearance

GARY MILLER

Gary Miller (born Neville Williams in Blackpool) was a straight ballad singer who, for a brief time, was considered to be on the fringe of the British rock scene. An ex-naval officer and World War 2 veteran, he made his unfruitful recording debut for the EMI-owned Columbia label in 1952. His first big break came when he joined the regulars on the fortnightly BBC Television show *Kaleidoscope* in 1953, which led to him signing with Philips Records, and a year later he was topping the cabaret bills on the famous Moss Empire circuit of variety theatres. The hits started only when Pye Records producer Alan A. Freeman (not to be confused with the disc jockey) took him under his wing in 1955. Miller was one of several acts to chart with contemporary pop smashes like the film theme 'Yellow Rose Of Texas' (which also charted for Mitch Miller with the American original, and Ronnie Hilton), the TV theme 'Robin Hood' (which Dick James hit with as well),' 'Garden Of Eden' (also a hit for Frankie Vaughan, Dick James and Joe Valino), and the Bacharach & David composition 'Story Of My Life' (which joined no less than three other versions on the Hit Parade by Michael Holliday, Dave King and Alma Cogan), and he usually succeeded in adding a certain zest and aggression that was lacking in the other versions. At the time of his 'Garden Of Eden' (1957) hit, the sensation-starved media went overboard about the fact that he actually dared to wear jeans on stage, and inevitably this rebellious action helped him to acquire a much larger following of teenage fans. Miller, who toured Britain with Buddy Holly & The Crickets in 1958, was certainly no true rocker, but was one of Britain's better beat ballad singers in the late 1950s.

Puttin' on the Style

ROCK'N'ROLL FASHION

Growing up in the 1950s in Britain meant swinging from shortages to prosperity, from rationing to a new age of affluence. In the late 1940s the younger generation followed adult fashion more casually but most were still expected to dress in a respectable manner, wearing styles similar to those worn by their parents.

Brighter and livelier fashions were longed for after the war and gradually things began to change. By the early 1950s young people's earnings had risen dramatically – by over 50 per cent since before the war – and so for the first time teenagers had money and became a force to be reckoned with. After handing over a pound or so to mum they were often left with more spare cash at the end of the week than their parents. Marketing men saw a whole new target area and for the first time they aimed at the teenager. Clothing manufacturers began to cash in on the young market by mass-producing inexpensive American-style clothes.

However, while some liberal-minded parents in the early 1950s were giving their teenage children more freedom with their choice of clothes, generally the young were expected to behave according the standards set by their elders. But the 'generation gap' was growing rapidly - teenagers were no longer relying on rules dictated by the middle-aged.

Fairgrounds and amusement arcades were the natural habitat of Teddy Girls (left) and Boys – both places rampant with the sound of rock'n'roll

1952 saw the first of the teenage gangs - the Teddy Boys or 'Teds' - and their distinctive look spread from working-class London to many corners of the UK. They were much feared at the time because of their delinquent lifestyle, and vandalism and gang warfare started to become commonplace in the streets and dance halls. Their uniform was a parody of fashion from the Edwardian era, consisting primarily of long drape jackets often with velvet cuffs and collars (the large pockets sometimes concealing weaponry like knuckledusters and bike chains). Outfits were often completed with Slim Jim shoestring ties, flashy waistcoats, drainpipe trousers, sometimes with 4" turn-ups, bright socks and thick crepe-soled 'beetle-crusher' or 'brothel creeper' shoes. The whole look wasn't cheap - the suit alone could cost three or four weeks' pay. Their partners, the Teddy Girls, tottered about on stiletto heels, often wearing slim pencil skirts, polo neck sweaters with three-quarter-length jackets or, alternatively, female 'zoot' suits.

Teddy Boys were a uniquely British fashion phenomenon, based on an 'Edwardian' look that had originally been aimed at the sons of the upper classes by smart Savile Row tailors

The hairstyle was very important, and there is some truth in the image people have today of Teddy Boys, with their Tony Curtis quiffs, continually combing their Brylcreemed hair into a DA (duck's arse) style and of Teddy Girls backcombing their foot-high bouffant 'beehive' hairdos.

In the mid-1950s very full circle skirts (often with stiff petticoats), which flared up when the wearer jived, became the desired dress for extrovert rock and rollers. They were often worn with tight-fitting, perky-collared shirt-style blouses which were anchored into the skirt with a wide waist-hugging belt. Tight-fitting capri or pirate pants, also called pedal-pushers, were also fashionable for females and denim jeans were becoming acceptable, boosted by stars such as Marilyn Monroe being photographed in them. All their trousers had side zips as front zips were considered 'naughty' for women. Hair was often pony-tailed or french-pleated, while lips could glow with lipstick shades like 'Hound Dog Orange' and 'Heartbreak Hotel Pink'. French film star Brigitte Bardot's appearance in a gingham bikini in 1956, and her gingham wedding dress in 1959, and American Carroll Baker's scanty short 'baby doll' pyjamas in the film *Baby Doll* from 1956 sparked off demands for similar provocative styles.

Designer Mary Quant opened her first Bazaar boutique in London's King's Road in 1955. Using a variety of the new man-made materials in bright colours, she produced innovative styles which rocked Britain. By the mid-1950s man-made fabrics had become increasingly available; materials like Terylene revolutionised the mass production of new styles; clothes were lighter in both weight and colour. Clothes could be washed and 'drip-dried' overnight without fear of shrinkage or running dyes (Mary Quant expanded into wholesale in 1961, and a few years later her 'mini' would help to make Britain the centre of the 1960s fashion scene).

In an era when women – and particularly teenage girls – were still meant to 'know their place', Teddy Girls seemed as much of a threat to the status quo because of their sheer audacity as their actual dress

Throughout the Fifties men moved slowly into the fashion limelight: pop stars were influencing styles and Elvis' look was copied everywhere. Some other teenage rebels, however, opted for fashion from films, such as jeans, T-shirts and leather jackets worn by Marlon Brando in the *The Wild One* (1953) and James Dean in *Rebel Without a Cause* (1955). By the end of the decade this had been taken a step further by the 'ton-up' kids - black leather-clad youths on motorbikes.

The hitch-hiking Beatnik was a new teenage archetype, which has persisted through Hippies, punks and other social drop-outs

Infamous in its day, the event at Hampstead's Paso Por Aqui Club in August 1960 attracted over a 1,000 'Ravers' and was described as the 'biggest Beatnik gathering ever'

By the late 1950s the wearing of 'Italian-style' clothes had become fashionable for men. The original Mods (also called Modernists or Individualists) were distinguished by their smart suits. Favouring this Italian-derived look, they wore short jackets ('bum-freezers'), tightish trousers, and pointed 'winklepicker' shoes. In 1957 the principal source was probably Glaswegian John Stephen's Beak Street shop. He moved round the corner in 1958, putting Carnaby Street on the map and making it the headquarters of Mods. By the mid- 1960s this small London side street was the international symbol of Swinging Britain. Modernists evolved into Mods in the 1960s and this is the image that endures; the gangs of lads in fur- trimmed parkas, on Vespa or Lambretta scooters customised with mirrors and lamps, clashing with leather-clad rockers on motorbikes (who had evolved from the late 1950s ton-up kids) on bank holidays at the seaside.

At the other extreme from the Mods was the casual look adopted by the nonconformist, anti-fashion, anti-establishment Beats (later called Beatniks), instantly recognisable by their longer, un-brushed hair. The 1950s marked the early beginnings of the 'permissive age' and the Beat philosophy was pacifism and free love, anarchy and socialism: Beatniks were the forerunners of the protesters and hippies in the 1960s. Bohemian black was the colour, worn by both boys and girls alike; the standard 'gear' for a boy was a duffle coat draped with a long scarf, a polo-neck sweater or baggy jumper, black trousers or jeans. A Beatnik girl wore much the same, often with corpse-white make-up and dark eye-liner, effecting the Left Bank look favoured by Paris Existentialists and actress Juliette Greco in particular.

In contrast to traditional night clubs, the jazz clubs that sprang up in the Fifties, like most of their clientele, were little concerned with creature comforts

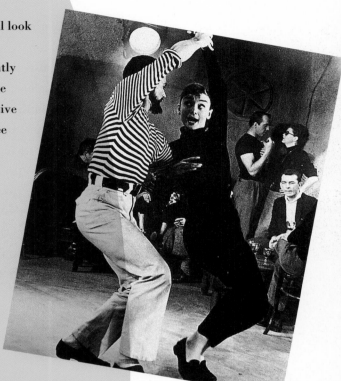

The elfin-short hair of film actress Audrey Hepburn was a style favoured among the female Beat fraternity

Britain was catching up with affluent America; a new generation had grown up who could hardly remember the postwar austerity: 'You've never had it so good' trumpeted Prime Minister Harold Macmillan in 1959. Young people of all social classes had developed definite ideas on what they wanted which were decidedly different from their counterparts of the conformist early 1950s. Now they had the confidence to create their own styles, and by the end of the decade British manufacturing and retail outlets were actively starting to promote new young designers catering for their young consumers.

Lipstick Traces

Rock'n'roll has always been tough'n'rough; a musical area where men call the shots and top-flight females are few and far between. Until the mid-1980s many female solo vocalists were simply the puppets of male record producers, having little or no say regarding the style or arrangement of their recordings; this situation was especially true in Britain during the 1950s. Alma Cogan's producer Wally Ridley explained, 'It was up to producers to find the right songs', adding: 'In the mid-1950s, that was a harder job than finding capable female singers to perform them.' In those pre-rock days, the essential attributes producers desired in a female artist seemed to be a pretty face, a wardrobe full of *Come Dancing* dresses, a recognisable voice, a continual smile and a subtle suggestion of sex appeal. Once a singer had a hit or two under her sequined belt, it was not unusual for her own views on songs to be taken into consideration, but it was almost unheard of for the lady to have the final say.

In 1955 Ireland's MOR ballad singer Ruby Murray was the UK's top recording artist, with a staggering seven Top 10 singles. However, Murray was in no hurry to climb on the rock bandwagon, as the music simply did not suit her voice or personality, and although at 20 she was younger than many rock singers, she was pushed into the background as r'n'r surged forward.

Eve Boswell – her image was that of the 'vivacious' popular singers of the early Fifties, soon to be eclipsed by the teen-appeal of a new generation of female vocalists

Perhaps influenced by Murray's expeditious exit, many astute A&R men decided that a little shot of rhythm & blues or rock'n'roll could be just what the doctor ordered to lengthen the chart lives of some of their female roster. The singers, to quote Alma Cogan, simply looked on these songs as 'happy-go-lucky rhythmic numbers', and a bevy of British belles including Cogan, Marion Ryan and Annette Klooger cheerfully covered little Frankie Lymon's 'Why Do Fools Fall In Love'. LaVern Baker's catchy 'Tra La La' was also well recorded on this side of the Atlantic by ladies like the Ted Heath Band's vocalist Klooger, Eve Boswell and Rose Brennan. Among the other R&B compositions that droves of UK female vocalists recorded were 'Two Hearts', 'Dance With Me Henry', 'Sincerely', and two other songs popularised Stateside by LaVern Baker, 'Tweedle Dee' and 'Lucky Lips'. Most of these records failed to sell in any noticeable quantities but they did prove that Britain's fairer sex were not afraid of tackling songs originally recorded by America's best R&B and rock acts. It also meant that otherwise obscure American songs were at least reaching the ears of British teenagers in some form. But only in the most elastic sense of the word could they be termed rock'n'roll records.

Arguably the first female performer launched as a rock singer in Britain was Pauline Shepherd in the autumn of 1956. Pye Records tagged this attractive teenage model 'The Princess Of Rock'. But, cute as she was, she did not seem to have a bopping bone in her body. It was around this time that the music business decided it was honour-bound to find 'The Female Elvis'. Among Britain's brave attempts at producing a prettier pelvis wiggler were Sandra Alfred, who burst on to the scene in 1958 with her somewhat forgettable recording of 'Rocket & Roll', Janice Peters who cut the aptly named 'This Little Girl's Gone Rockin' (Ruth Brown had recorded it first), and over-the-top performer Kerry Martin, who sang 'Stroll Me'. Each was welcomed with a deafening silence by a public who were more than happy with just one Elvis.

In the late 1950s the only British competition for America's first ladies of rock and pop, Connie Francis and Brenda Lee, came from Shirley Bassey and Petula Clark. Wales-born Bassey was unique in Britain; she was a cabaret artist with no equals outside America, and her MOR records sold very well both before and after The Beatles' arrival on the scene. Clark, although only in her late 20s, had been a celebrity in Britain since the late Forties. Her trio of contemporary pop Top 20 hits in 1957-8 made her Britain's most successful female singer since Ruby Murray. Although she never saw herself as a rock singer, Clark admitted 'the pop business needed a shake up, and rock and skiffle have done a tremendous amount of good.' Clark not only added to her UK hit score in the early 1960s but went on to become an international chart regular later in the decade and one of the biggest selling female artists of the era.

Along with Brenda Lee, American Connie Francis led the female field in the rock era, although few of her records could be called rock'n'roll. Among those that did qualify were 1958's 'Stupid Cupid' and 'Lipstick On Your Collar' in the following year

The lack of pop queens in Britain was certainly not due to a shortage of aspiring candidates. Valerie Masters, Valerie Shane, Frankie Vaughan's sister-in-law and ex-secretary Joyce Shock, Lorie Mann, Maxine Daniels (who had sung with Tony Crombie & His Rockets), Larry Parnes' discovery Sally Kelly, Lorne Lesley, Lorrae Desmond and organist Cherry Wainer (an honours graduate from the Miles Of Smiles Academy who had been called 'The Female Liberace' in 1956) were among the ladies-in-waiting. Their failure may have been due to a lacklustre choice of material, dated productions or vocal performance or simply that many of them seemed to dress more like teenagers' mothers than teenagers. Whatever the reason, success was a stranger to them.

Petula Clark's 'Little Shoemaker' was voted one of the top three all-time choices on the long-running *Children's Favourites* radio show

The 1960s brought with them a wave of new British female singers, with 14-year-old schoolgirl Helen Shapiro leading the onslaught. Unlike most of her predecessors, Shapiro recorded original songs (composed for her by John Schroeder) and her success in Britain was staggering, her first four singles all making the Top 5. Although this formidable chanteuse's records were on a par with any by American female singers at the time, she only managed one week in the US chart when her UK No. 1 'Walkin' Back To Happiness' peaked at No. 100 there in 1961!

Whilst schoolgirl Shapiro stiffed Stateside, another British teenager, Hayley Mills, took the USA by storm. The actress' recording of 'Let's Get Together' from her film *The Parent Trap* gave this 14-year-old a Stateside Top 10 entry. The song – which Mills described as 'Quite gay', though she warned 'If you hear it too much you are likely to go mad' – also later climbed into the UK Top 20. While Mills may seem an unlikely candidate for inclusion in a book on British beat, it should be noted that in the film she and her identical twin sister (also played by Miss Mills) sang and played guitar with a Beatles styled mop-top haircut, and that one of her rock/pop hit's major hooks was its 'Yeah yeah yeah' refrain!

Child film prodigy Hayley Mills (above) was a record star too by the age of 14

The altogether more 'cookie' Louise Cordet adopted the 'beat' look that was fashionable in the early Sixties

1962 was a good year for the girls. Sixteen-year-old, pigtailed private school pupil Louise Cordet had a one-off hit with 'I'm Just A Baby', a song that British composer Jerry Lordan had written with Brenda Lee in mind. Her cute and breathily sexy interpretation gave Lordan his sixth Top 20 entry. It was another example of a commercial British song that should have succeeded on the other side of the Atlantic and, had it been released after The Beatles broke down the barriers a couple of years later, might well have been a hit there too.

Keeping up 1962's cute quota were petite Carol Deene (who starred with Acker Bilk in 'Band Of Thieves') and Valerie Mountain, who both charted with the theme song from the British teen flick *Some People*; and actress Wendy Richard (who now plays Pauline Fowler in *EastEnders*) played the foil to actor/singer Mike Sarne on his No. 1 hit 'Come Outside'. Incidentally, Richard, who was then aged 18, said about the session, 'I thought I was only going to the studio to do a voice over for a TV commercial!' She added 'I never received any royalties from that chart-topping single.'

Up-and-coming new names in those early years of the swinging sixties included attractive Kathy Kirby, a Monroe lookalike. who had been singing professionally since 1956, Julie Grant, a 16-year-old, who had once beaten Helen Shapiro in a talent competition, and young Irish colleen Cloda (later spelled Clodagh) Rodgers who had just signed to Decca. Also being tipped for stardom were teenager Suzy Cope, ex-Vernon's Girl Lynn Cornell and Scotland's Lena Martell, while in Liverpool Cilla Black was building a fan following via regular appearances with groups like Kingsize Taylor & The Dominoes, The Big Three and The Beatles. Meanwhile, across the Atlantic, Aretha Franklin, Gladys Knight and Tina Turner were already having chart success.

Most of this new breed of British girl vocalists were less obviously 'dressy' than their 1950s counterparts. In response to a genuinely teen-oriented fashion market for the first time, they cultivated a 'nice girl' next door image, and looked more like the average British (though some would say American) teenager. They may have lacked some of the finery of the Fifties females, in fact in many ways the way they dressed could be said to be an early hint at a sexual equality to come; but true even-handedness in the way women are dealt with is still far from prevalent in the music business, and back in the early Sixties this move to a more casual look was more cute 'girl next door' than threatening 'tom-boy next door'.

Lynn Cornell's only chart entry was the 1960 movie-theme 'Never On Sunday' which crept in at Number Thirty

Alma Cogan's well-remembered image was one of the early examples of a pop star being promoted via television rather than radio – a real sign of the times

ALMA COGAN

The singer known as 'The girl with the chuckle in her voice' was born in Sussex, and was one of Britain's most popular entertainers in the 1950s. She is remembered almost as much for her glamorous self-designed dresses as she is for her recordings. After failing an audition for Ted Heath's Orchestra in 1948 Cogan had some minor acting roles before signing to HMV Records in 1952. Her choice of material was seldom original, although she always put her unique stamp on anything she recorded. Her string of Top 10 hits in the 1950s included ' Bell Bottom Blues' (a US hit for Teresa Brewer), 'I Can't Tell A Waltz From a Tango' (Patti Page's American charter), ' Dreamboat' (previously recorded by The Paulette Sisters), which was the only No. 1 in the decade by a British female artist, and 'Never Do A Tango With An Eskimo', written for her by UK composer Tommie Connor. It would be wrong to call Cogan a rock performer but, as she said, 'if you define rock'n'roll as insistent rhythmic swing, then I've sung rock.' Among the songs she recorded from the rock area were Charlie Gracie's 'Fabulous', Fats Domino's 'I'm In Love Again', LaVern Baker's 'Tweedle Dee', Bobby Rydell's 'We Got Love', and the almost obligatory pair from the Marty Robbins' catalogue, 'The Story Of My Life' and 'Stairway Of Love'. The lady who was always dressed up to the nines and aimed at the Top 10 died of cancer in 1966, aged only 34.

P E T U L A   C L A R K

Surrey-born Petula Clark first appeared on BBC radio in 1942, when she was only nine years old. She was an instant success, and was appearing in the first of over 20 films by the time she was 12. Clark became a regular on the TV show *Cabaret* in 1946, and three years later released her debut record, 'Put Your Shoes On Lucy', on Columbia. In the following year she joined Polygon Records (part owned by her father Leslie), and was voted Top Woman On TV. In the early 1950s Clark cut covers of such US hits as 'Cold, Cold Heart', 'Tennessee Waltz', and the Italian song 'Poppa Piccolino' before finally charting with the French composition 'The Little Shoemaker' in 1954. In 1957 her recording of Jodie Sand's beat ballad 'With All My Heart' introduced the youthful-looking veteran to the teen romance market, and she followed it up the charts with equally catchy, up-beat versions of the Shepherd Sisters' 'Alone' and The Twin Tunes Quintet's 'Baby Lover'. Petula admitted, 'I wasn't too keen on the first two songs but I thought "Baby Lover" was cute, and too good a novelty to miss.' Before the end of the decade she had relocated to France and was soon the belle of the boulevards too. In 1961, her version of the German hit 'Sailor' topped some UK charts, and she followed it into the Top 5 with another German number 'Romeo'. Clark also had one of the most successful twist records with a bi-

Petula Clark , already a seasoned professional, singing at a ball in 1954

lingual treatment of Lee Dorsey's 'Ya Ya' in 1962. Her amazing career reached its peak in 1965-7, when her partnership with producer/songwriter Tony Hatch resulted in a long run of top-selling transatlantic hits. In 1966 her recording of 'Downtown' not only became the first single by a British female to top the American chart for 14 years, but also collected the Grammy for Best Rock'n'Roll Record, while she was voted America's Most Popular Female Singer by radio DJs. In 1988 the lady who has now spent over 50 years in the business saw a re-mixed version of 'Downtown' zoom up the British charts, giving her an unprecedented 34-year span of Top 10 UK hits.

HELEN SHAPIRO

Londoner Helen Shapiro was only 14 when Norrie Paramor's right-hand man John Schroeder heard her at Maurice Berman's singing school. He was amazed that a girl of her age possessed such a deep, mature voice and used such good phrasing. Paramor was equally impressed and signed her to EMI. Her first single was Schroeder's composition, 'Don't Treat Me Like A Child', which took the schoolgirl into the Top 5 in 1961. She was instantly tagged Britain's answer to Brenda Lee. 'That doesn't bother me at all', she said. 'Brenda is a great singer – so I take it as a compliment. However, my aim is to be Britain's Helen Shapiro, and to the best of my knowledge I have not been influenced by Brenda.' Her follow up, 'You Don't Know', composed by Schroeder and Mike Hawker hit No. 1, and her third release, another Schroeder and Hawker song, 'Walkin' Back To Happiness', amassed record advance orders (for a British female) of over 300,000 copies. The song quickly became her second chart topper, and like its predecessor sold over a million copies world-wide. Before she was 16, Shapiro had headlined British and European tours, been voted the UK's Top Female Artist, hit the Top 3 with her debut album, Tops With Me (which included a version of Brenda Lee's 'Sweet Nuthin's'), and appeared in two films, *Play It Cool* (with Billy Fury), and *It's Trad, Dad!*, in which she starred with Craig Douglas (the soundtrack album also climbed into the Top 3).

With a deep voice that hinted at someone of more mature years, Helen Shapiro was by far the most successful British girl singer in the early years of the Sixties

1963 started with a UK tour, on which she was supported by The Beatles, and a three day recording session in Nashville, on which Elvis' backing vocal group, the Jordanaires, supported her. However, as fast as the Beatles' star was ascending, Helen's was descending and, despite her youth, she was soon discarded by teenagers as 'yesterday's news'. Jazz music had always been Helen's first love, and before her hits she had sung with a jazz band led by her brother Ronnie. She confessed 'I'm happy singing pop now but one of these days I'd like to make a living singing jazz, blues and that kind of music.' Her wish came true, perhaps a little earlier than she and most critics expected, and she is still making a good living in that field of music.

English Eccentrics

THE WILD AND THE WEIRD

The popular music scene in the early 1950s was ruled by a brigade of well-dressed ballad singers and crooners, the vast majority of whom had interchangeable and fairly unexciting stage acts. The people in their 20s and 30s who crowded into concerts by the likes of Como, Cole and Crosby were content to hear their idols croon and to see the minimum of movement. Eccentric performers were very thin on the ground.

Probably the wildest of them all, Little Richard was a direct influence on energetic rockers like Willie Harris and Dave 'Screamin' Lord' Sutch

Then along came rock'n'roll, which was aimed at adolescents, who naturally wanted to rebel against what had gone before, and if what they liked broke the rules of stagecraft, and alienated their parents' generation, then all the better. Bill Haley's sax man Rudy Pompilli playing horizontally while fellow Comet Al Rex rode the stand-up bass shocked as many people as it delighted. Elvis' pelvic gyrations, highlighting the hose pipe down his trousers, horrified many, and Little Richard's screaming and shouting, while standing at, and often on, the piano, or the sight of Jerry Lee Lewis de-tuning his piano as he attacked the keys with a vengeance was the last straw for most 'good music' lovers. Other mid-1950s US eccentrics who should not be forgotten include Screamin' Jay Hawkins and Gene Vincent. Hawkins, whose act revolved around coffins and skulls, is still thought to have been 'weird' and 'unhealthy', while greasy Gene, who dragged his gammy leg around behind him, and his hoodlum friends, the Blue Caps, brought all the excitement of gang warfare to the stage. To mention all the other American acts that were considered eccentric would fill the book; to the older generation almost every rock'n'roll performer appeared to have just escaped from an asylum.

60

Meanwhile, back in the UK, a public whose only sight of a left-field act had been the wild pianist Morgan 'Thunderclap' Jones in the mid-1950s (who stripped while pounding out boogie music on the 88), initially considered that Tommy Steele's chirpy beat music was so unusual that he too was regarded as an eccentric. Performers like Cliff Richard, Marty Wilde and Billy Fury, who followed in Steele's wake, may have been thought to go 'over the top' with their displays of exhibitionism and sexual magnetism, but only a few people would have tagged them 'eccentrics'. However, Britain, which has a certain reputation for harbouring more eccentrics per square mile than most other places, was not short of its own bizarre rockers, and the weirdest and wildest of the bunch were Wee Willie Harris and Screamin' Lord Sutch, both of whom knew they couldn't win young girls' hearts with their looks and so made no concessions to normality during their acts.

Both Harris and Sutch had emerged from the 2 I's coffee bar in Soho. As a performer, Wee Willie Harris inspired comparisons with Little Richard, but it was his outrageous image that made the public take notice. The singer/pianist wore a bright red drape coat with his name emblazoned on the back, and to top that off, at the suggestion of his manager Paul Lincoln, he had dyed his hair shocking pink (this dyed hair gimmick was later copied by rival singer, Larry Page, and DJ Jimmy Saville). Harris' records never made chart headway, but thanks to touring with Cliff Richard, and his regular appearances on *6.5 Special*, he became one the best-known performers in Britain.

A hip hooray – the Earl of Wharncliffe, a member of the aristocracy slumming it behind a drum kit as the 'Rock'n'Roll Earl'

Watching Screamin' Lord Sutch on stage could be a frightening and dangerous experience. Sutch, who had 18-inch-long hair (long before The Beatles and Stones started the movement towards flowing locks for boys), wore a top hat and tails and looked every inch as menacing as 'Jack The Ripper', whom he sang about. He would leap into the audience wielding a knife or axe (the real thing, not a guitar) and giving the distinct impression that he was hell bent on hacking to death anyone who stood in his way. Not surprisingly, screaming girls ran in all directions, and even their brave boyfriends gave Sutch plenty of room. Sutch was such a unique character that he became the

61

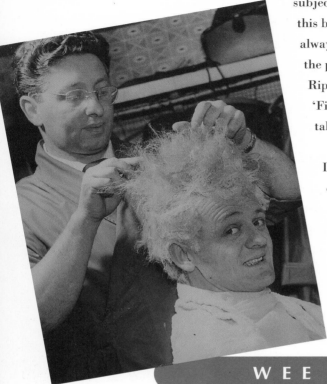

subject of numerous newspaper stories like, 'Would you let this boy marry your daughter?' Being Sutch's pianist was always a hazardous occupation, as it meant you played the prostitute who was murdered during his Jack The Ripper routine. The one-eyed boogie boy, Freddy 'Fingers' Lee, who was such a pianist, was once hospitalised by Sutch.

In pre-Beatles days no other British performers came close to the overall lunacy of Harris and Sutch, although some critics might include 'the sheik of shake', Dickie Pride, alongside them. In the 1960s, the decade that really put British music on the map, there were several acts that might be regarded as odd-balls but none are remembered with such warmth as these charismatic and kookie characters.

Wee Willie Harris during one of his well-publicised visits to the hairdressers

WEE WILLIE HARRIS

Charles William Harris, who was born in Bermondsey in 1933, played the piano in London pubs as Fingers Harris. With the advent of rock'n'roll, he became Wee Willie Harris (his manager Paul Lincoln suggested the 'Wee' part), and his 'larger than life' appearances on *6.5. Special* helped make him one of the most widely recognised rock'n'rollers. His first single coupled the Timmie Rogers original, 'Back To School Again', with his own composition, 'Rockin' At The Two I's', a paean to the famous coffee bar where he had previously performed. His other early releases were also covers, 'Love Bug Crawl' (first cut by Missouri rocker Jimmy Edwards), the semi-instrumental pop/novelty 'Got A Match' (a US Top 40 hit for The Daddy-O's) and 'Wild One'/'Little Bitty Girl' (a double-sided cover of a Bobby Rydell single). On stage, Harris would don a leopard skin, bowler hat and cane to perform Neil Sedaka's 'I Go Ape' (Harris' version was released in the US), and during the number he would run into the audience, chasing girls with his stage club. When rock'n'roll became unfashionable, Harris was adamant that 'As long as I get applause from rock, I'm a rocker', and when asked about his future added, 'My career will last as long as my hair. If I keep my thatch nice and rosy, my future will be rosy too.' Harris, who looked more than the 24 years old that he claimed, may not have been one of the great rock vocalists of his era but he was a good showman. Although he never made a hit record, he is mentioned in the lyric of Ian Dury's Top 3 hit, 'Reasons To Be Cheerful (Part 3)'. Reflecting on his 40-year career, he says, 'It's a pity I've never found anyone really interested in making records with me because I do think I've got a good recording voice.'

SCREAMIN' LORD SUTCH

Screamin' Lord Sutch, who was born plain David Sutch in 1940, developed his wild act on the small stages of London coffee bars. He formed the Savages in 1960 and its personnel has included Ritchie Blackmore, Nicky Hopkins, Paul Nicholas and Matthew Fisher. He claims to have influenced the Rolling Stones, Alice Cooper and Michael Jackson ('Thriller') and, as leader of the official Monster Raving Loony Party, he remains still crazy after all these years. Sutch is the UK's longest-serving political leader and he stands for parliament at every opportunity. His platform, which originally had conviction (votes at 18, the introduction of commercial radio), has degenerated into one-liners (hedgehog parks, ski-slopes down the EC butter mountain, etc.). He says, 'I still perform "I'm A Hog For You Baby" with a toilet seat and a pig's mask and I dedicate it to whoever's in power.' In 1961 Joe Meek produced Sutch's first record, ' 'Til The Following Night' (coupled with a tremendous version of 'Good Golly Miss Molly') which was absolutely unique, and is not only a classic of the rock-horror genre but also among the best rock'n'roll records ever cut in Britain. It goes without saying that this single was too wild for UK radio and, like the equally powerful 'Jack The Ripper' single later, it failed to achieve the air play necessary for a hit. In 1970 Jeff Beck, Jimmy Page and John Bonham joined his Lordship on the album, Lord Sutch And His Heavy Friends, which reached the US Top 100. When asked about his lack of hits, he commented, 'A lot of people who've had two or three big records are completely forgotten, but I've still got a cult following.'

A record company promotional hand-out for Dave 'Screaming Lord' Sutch: the handwritten message says 'About that cheque that bounced!'

This Here's The Story...

T h e   S k i f f l e   B o o m

Skiffle was a home-made music, with no set boundaries, and was by its very nature amateurish. The reason that it caught on like wildfire could have been its folksy simplicity, the fact that the instruments required were not expensive and that a reasonable sound could be achieved with little musical experience. *NME* said, 'Never before has a musical craze been so easy to "do it yourself" '. It was arguably the most influential UK musical trend of all time; however, unlike most other trends its success can be attributed to the records of one main contributor, Lonnie Donegan.

Skiffle's attraction was that it was a do-it-yourself music, and all over the country groups sprung up who could play virtually anywhere. Here the Skiffle Gypsies, endorsed by the *Daily Mail* newspaper, hold a well-publicised session on Brighton beach

In 1961 Lonnie Donegan received not only a Gold Disc for his US hit 'Does Your Chewing Gum Lose Its Flavour', but also a belated one for his 1956 transatlantic Top Ten hit 'Rock Island Line' – presented by the 'Old Groaner' himself Bing Crosby

According to Donegan, 'Skiffle is part of the phrase "skiffle party", which was a slang way of saying " rent party" '. He told the *NME* in 1957, 'These parties were held principally in the Chicago districts in the 1920s, their purpose being the obvious one of raising money to pay the rent.' People turned up with their own food, drink and often musical instrument and the music that came out of these gatherings was an improvised and informal mixture of the blues, folk, gospel, jazz and the popular music of the time. The sound would depend on who arrived and what instruments they brought with them. Donegan stressed, 'There are obviously no genuine recordings of skiffle music proper from those days, as the very presence of microphones destroys the essential informality of this type of music.' When recording, Lonnie explained, 'I estimate the amount of folk content, jazz content and informality which would be the result of the song in question being sung at one of these gatherings.' He said that skiffle in the 1950s was 'a potpourri of styles and sources, the mixture of which is at the discretion of the singer. The instrumentation of the skiffle group cannot be typical or specific, since any and most instruments were used at these parties. The guitar, though, was without doubt the most frequently used instrument, and the voice the principal one.' However, Donegan was adamant that, despite media claims, 'the washboard was only seldom used in such sessions.'

However, to confuse the matter of its origin, *Rolling Stone* magazine simply says, 'Skiffle was New Orleans jazz and jug band music', and the purist poll-winning traditional jazz band leader Ken Colyer is said to have 'discovered' skiffle on a field trip to New Orleans in 1952, when he was collecting folklore and material from the birthplace of jazz.

There is no doubt that in Britain it was Colyer's band, with Donegan as the vocalist, who first featured skiffle in their act. When the group's trombonist Chris Barber left to form his own group, Donegan went with him, and before long both Colyer's and Barber's bands featured a skiffle segment in their shows. In 1954 Barber's band released an album, New Orleans Joys, that included two skiffle tracks featuring Donegan, and in mid-1955 Colyer's skiffle group (which at times included Alexis Korner, who would go on to form the seminal British R&B group Blues Incorporated) released the skiffle single, 'Take This Hammer'. Both records were bought by the jazz band's fans but meant less than nothing to the general public.

Lonnie Donegan was catapulted from the relative obscurity of the rhythm section of a jazz band to fully-fledged superstardom literally in a matter of a few short months

When Decca announced that they were issuing one of Barber's 18-month-old album tracks, 'Rock Island Line', credited to the Lonnie Donegan Skiffle Group, the odds against it being a transatlantic Top 10 hit were at least a million to one, and only the insane or the fanciful would have dared to predict that it would launch a musical craze that would sweep Britain like no other before or since. True, the old Leadbelly song which Donegan half recited and half sang at breakneck speed had been a popular live number in the Barber Band's skiffle section, but no one could have foreseen the events that followed.

When 'Rock Island Line' entered the British charts in January 1956 it came as a surprise to almost everyone. One British record paper declared, 'There's no accounting for taste'. *NME*'s astute columnist Alley Cat noted that, 'Here was further proof of how unpredictable the music industry is', and Donegan himself said scornfully, 'I don't think it's a particularly good recording, and even asked to have it withdrawn when I first heard it.' Bemused critics searched for reasons for the success of this 'clearly uncommercial' record. Some felt that it had to be due in part to its appearance on the scene when narrative records were being tipped as the next big thing (remember 'The Shifting Whispering Sands'?). Others said its arrival at a time when rock'n'roll was starting to break wide open had helped, with some suggesting that it was selling 'on its title alone'. Either way, the record rode into the British Top 10 and, when released across the Atlantic, shipped 150,000 in its first 10 days. Here was a Scottish-born, London-bred performer (whom the Americans tagged an 'Irish Hillbilly') mimicking the accent of a black American, taking coals to Newcastle along the Rock Island Line, and steaming into the US Top 10, alongside Elvis Presley's debut single 'Heartbreak Hotel'. Incidentally, both these singles had the dubious honour of being the subjects of hit singles by the 'prince of pop parody' Stan Freberg. 'I was thrilled to learn about Freberg's record', Lonnie said. 'I take it to be an indirect compliment – it gave me the biggest laugh I've had for years.'

Part of Les Hobeaux skiffle group entertain some jolly hand-jivers in what the press report at the time described as a 'gay skiffle cellar' in London's Soho

The artist who had perhaps the greatest influence on the British skiffle performers was singer/songwriter Huddie 'Leadbelly' Ledbetter, whose catalogue of classic blues and folk songs was often raided in the skiffle era. It was Leadbelly, for instance, who originally recorded Donegan's hits 'Rock Island Line', 'Bring A Little Water Sylvie',

'Have A Drink On Me' and 'Pick A Bale Of Cotton'. Black performers were not the only source of material for the 1950s skifflers' songs, since many came from the country field and a lot from white folk singers, particularly Woody Guthrie. Guthrie (who a few years later would be acclaimed by US folkies such as Bob Dylan) composed several songs that Donegan re-arranged and had hits with,'Gamblin' Man', 'Dead Or Alive', 'Grand Coolie Dam' and 'Sally Don't You Grieve'.

In May 1956 the attraction of America and the draw of the dollar became too much, and Donegan departed Barber's Band and headed west, guitar in hand, to make his solo stage debut 3,000 miles from home at Brooklyn's swish Town & Country Club. In their wisdom, the Musicians Union decreed Donegan could not play his trusty instrument on an American stage, but even this did not spoil his 10-week Stateside sojourn. During his stay he appeared on the Perry Como TV show (with fellow guest Ronald Reagan), worked alongside top rock acts as Chuck Berry, Pat Boone, Clyde McPhatter, Frankie Lymon & The Teenagers and LaVern Baker, and on some dates was backed by rockabilly legends the Johnny Burnette Trio. Before returning to Britain he had seen his face on the cover of a leading US music trade magazine *Cash Box*, and watched his follow-up, 'Lost John', narrowly miss the US Top 40. He came home a conquering hero, finally formed his own skiffle group (minus a washboard, which he disliked), and quickly proved to any doubters he was no five-minute wonder by bringing down the house wherever he played. Talking about his sudden success, he was adamant about one subject: 'I have not gone commercial. It's just that the kind of act I do has become commercial.' Also in 1956 Lonnie became the first British performer to reach the singles chart with not only an EP but also with an album ! Among the other skiffle recordings released that year were Ken Colyer's Skiffle Group with two more train songs, 'Streamline Train' and 'Downbound Train', Beryl Bryden's Backroom Skiffle (led by Lonnie's old washboard player) with the story about railroad engineer 'Casey Jones', and the Vipers' 'Ain't You Glad'/'Pick a Bale Of Cotton'. None of these charted. The year closed with Donegan being voted runner-up to Dickie Valentine as Outstanding British Music Personality.

Britain tested its first H-Bomb in 1957, but it wasn't the only thing making a big bang that year. Skiffle exploded, and before you could say, 'Mum, can I borrow your washboard?', groups were mushrooming in every corner of the land. In March

Sheet music featuring the Chas McDevitt Skiffle Group. For a short time hitherto amateur skifflers were plunged into the pop mainstream, with all the Tin Pan Alley ballyhoo that went with it

Altogether, Lonnie Donegan had thirty five UK Top Fifty chart entries between 1956 and 1962

Strictly speaking a country and western singer, American Johnny Duncan was launched in Great Britain via the skiffle boom, but retained his 'bluegrass' image right down to the flamboyant cowboy shirts and sixguns

Johnny Duncan's Yuletide hit 'Footprints In The Snow' entered the chart twice on either side of Christmas 1957

BBC TV's youth-accented show, *6.5 Special*, was launched, and many of the acts featured were skiffle groups. In June BBC radio acknowledged the importance of skiffle by replacing 30 minutes of theatre organ music at 10.00 on Saturday mornings with *Saturday Skiffle Club*. On the record front, The Vipers skiffle group soon joined Donegan in the Top 10 and in no time they were joined by the Chas McDevitt Skiffle Group (fronted by Nancy Whiskey) with 'Freight Train', plus American Johnny Duncan and his Blue Grass Boys (a hybrid act that straddled the fence between blue grass, rockabilly and skiffle), who steamed into the Top 10 with their second single, yet another train song, 'Last Train To San Fernando' (previously recorded by Bobby Short).

For a while America, too, kept up its interest in skiffle, and in the spring Lonnie Donegan found himself playing at Madison Square Gardens as part of a 21-day US tour supporting the world-famous basketball team, the Harlem Globetrotters. When he returned he shared top billing at the prestigious London Palladium for two weeks with top US vocal group The Platters, and starred with McDevitt, Whiskey and Bob Cort's Skiffle Group at the first *Skiffle Festival* at the Royal Albert Hall. Before long Donegan scored his second successive No. 1 with the novelty song 'Putting On The Style', coupled with a frenzied version of 'Gamblin' Man'. In May Nancy Whiskey was whisked off to America to promote 'Freight Train', which was 'goin' so fast' up the US chart. American reporters wanted to know all about skiffle, and Whiskey says, 'They couldn't believe we had borrowed American folk music, added something to it, and turned it into a commercial proposition.' Two months later Chas, Nancy and washboard wizard Marc Sharratt were performing in the US on Ed Sullivan's *Toast Of The Town* show (on the same evening that the Everly Brothers made their debut), backed by a trio of Nashville's top country pickers. During their stay in the USA (which was cut short when it was discovered they did not have the correct work permits), the Scottish skifflers also played at the famous Palisades Park alongside several top R&B and doo-wop acts.

Skiffle competitions took place throughout the length and breadth of Britain, and there were no shortage of entrants, since groups were more plentiful than the trains about which they often sang, with one writer estimating that there were about 1,000 skiffle combos in the London area alone. Every club and coffee house had an embarrassment of groups to call upon - the scene was thriving, as any guitar manufacturer at the time would tell you. Even bill-topping MOR star Dickie Valentine covered 'Putting On The Style', the 'square' Stargazers released 'Skiffling Dogs', and Ron Goodwin & His Orchestra released the George Martin-produced 'Skiffling Strings' – all confident indications that 'the biggest musical craze Britain has ever known', as *NME* called it, had nothing but a very bright future.

However, much to everyone's surprise, the track was already running out for the fast-moving skiffle express and for all those who had jumped aboard after Donegan had taken it through the toll gate. Before the summer of 1957 was over only Donegan, the 'Sultan of Skiffle', was still reaching the Top 20 – in all he had five entries that year. The follow-ups from The Vipers, McDevitt and Duncan all failed to emulate the success of their debut hits, and releases by such highly touted skifflers as Bob Cort (who not only made a handful of singles, including the train song theme from *6.5 Special* and Chuck Berry's 'School Day', but also published a book *How To Skiffle Successfully*), Sonny Stewart's Skiffle Kings, Jimmy Jackson's Rock'n'Skiffle' (with a version of Eddie Cochran's hit 'Sitting In The Balcony'), ex-Donegan sideman Dickie Bishop & His Side Kicks, and Ken Colyer (whose 'House Rent Stomp' went back to the roots of the music) all failed to capture the public's imagination. Don Lang's skiffle album was also on a clear hiding to nothing, as were releases from newer skiffle ensembles like the multi-national Les Hobeaux, The 219 Skiffle Group, The Station Skiffle Group and The Delta Skiffle Group. There were also unrewarding releases from such acts as The Avon Cities Skiffle Group and The Original City Ramblers. 1957 was the year that the skiffle craze was born, reached maturity and was given its last rites – a little like the life of a moth.

The rush-released Terry Dene movie, *The Golden Disc*, which hit the streets in early 1958, included skifflers Les Hobeaux (whose Brian Gregg was later in Johnny Kidd's Pirates as well as Colin Hick's Cabin Boys, Terry Dene's Dene Aces and The Tornados) and Sonny Stewart & The Skiffle Kings, but this extra exposure did not give skiffle the boost it needed - its appeal was evaporating fast. The media asked 'Is skiffle dying?', one critic adding that, 'people had become too sophisticated for the rough-hewn basic strum and scrape style of skiffle' and proclaiming, 'the ballads are back, and

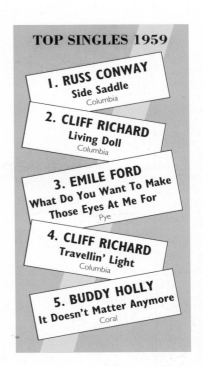

TOP SINGLES 1959

1. **RUSS CONWAY**
   Side Saddle
   Columbia

2. **CLIFF RICHARD**
   Living Doll
   Columbia

3. **EMILE FORD**
   What Do You Want To Make Those Eyes At Me For
   Pye

4. **CLIFF RICHARD**
   Travellin' Light
   Columbia

5. **BUDDY HOLLY**
   It Doesn't Matter Anymore
   Coral

Russell Quay's City Ramblers distanced themselves from the more 'commercial' skiffle outfits by describing themselves as a 'spasm band' with an authentic instrumentation that included kazoos and the much-maligned washboard

skiffle is sunk.' If this produced a feeling of déjà vu, it was because such critics had said similar things about rock'n'roll less than 12 months earlier. This time, however, they had hit the nail on the head. Astute skiffle groups were chopping up their tea-chest bases for firewood and returning their washboards to the laundries. The Vipers sensed a change was in the air, dropped the word skiffle from their name, and started to incorporate more standard folk songs and country numbers into their act. Their vocalist Wally Whyton explained, 'We want to feel free to broaden our scope. In other words, we don't want people to think that skiffle is all we can play.' Chas McDevitt felt 'skiffle is finding its own level' and explained that his group was 'trying to widen our appeal by playing cabaret type spots at dance halls.' He had also added pop and rock songs like 'My Special Angel',' That'll Be The Day' and 'Wake Up Little Susie' to the act, explaining, 'Skiffle is just a style of playing and almost any form of music can be played in that style - within reason.'

Record companies continued to release skiffle singles, but their major promotional push favoured rock records. Skifflers (other than Donegan) were passé to the public, and they and their train songs were sent back to the sidings. Donegan, the sole survivor, said, 'You must remember that jazz- call it improvisation if you like – is an essential part of skiffle. Without this all you have is simple folk music, which is not saleable to the masses. If so-called skiffle musicians can't improvise, they aren't playing skiffle. I feel that perhaps we are the only group now who understand what skiffle really is.'

The Lonnie Donegan Skiffle Group were true superstars in their day. Here Lonnie (second left) is filming at Shepperton Studios with his longest-standing personnel that included Jimmy Currie (left) on lead guitar and double bass player Mickey Ashman (far right)

Skiffle was not only rejected by the public, it was also despised by the trad jazz scene from where it had emerged. It was bound for the scrap heap, along with the steam trains it often eulogised. Many clubs and coffee bars where skiffle had reigned supreme became (or reverted back to) traditional jazz clubs, and before long these same clubs would be the breeding ground for another musical craze – trad.

Skiffle's time in the limelight was short, and its successful exponents could be counted on the fingers of one hand, but never in the history of British music have so many been influenced by so few. It almost literally put guitars into the hands of the generation of teenagers who went on to create the British rock scene of the Sixties.

L O N N I E   D O N E G A N

Lonnie Donegan (born Anthony Donegan in Glasgow), who had been an avid collector of folk and blues records since his youth, formed the Tony Donegan Jazz Band in 1951 after being demobbed from the Army. In June 1952, he appeared at the Royal Festival Hall with his idol, blues singer Lonnie Johnson, and from then on Donegan adopted Johnson's Christian name. Shortly afterwards he joined his old Army friend Chris Barber, whose band soon evolved into Ken Colyer's Jazzmen. Before long, Donegan, who played guitar and banjo, was fronting a small unit within that band singing his own brand of skiffle, and in 1953 he made his first (unreleased) recordings in that style. Barber left Colyer in 1954, and Donegan and his skiffle section joined Barber's new trad band. A year later Donegan's recordings of 'Rock Island Line' and 'John Henry' were included on a Chris Barber LP (the other musicians on the skiffle tracks being Barber – whose main instrument was the trombone – on bass and washboard player Beryl Bryden). Bob Crabb, an executive at Decca Records, had a feeling about the former track, and released it as a single at the tail end of 1955. When it rocketed into the Top 10 no one was more suprised than the level headed Donegan, who insisted,' I have no intention of being tempted away from the Chris Barber Band for a precarious career as a solo artist. I don't want to be swept along on the tide of the latest gimmick and then left high and dry when it wears off.' However, such was the demand for his services in the United States that he reluctantly abandoned his secure and well-paid job with Barber. Donegan, who received only a minimal session fee for singing 'Rock Island Line' (although he did receive writer's royalties for arranging both sides of the record), signed to Pye Records and to many people's surprise the hits continued. Donegan, who initially said, 'I am merely attempting to recreate the work of "authentic" folk singers like Lonnie Johnson, Leadbelly and Muddy Waters', expanded his horizons, and thanks in part to the addition of some humorous novelty numbers to his repertoire, this energetic entertainer far outlasted all his skiffle contemporaries, and had an unprecedented succession of hits between 1956 and 1962. Among his 26 UK Top 20 hits were the chart toppers 'Cumberland Gap', 'Gamblin' Man'/'Putting On The Style' and 'My Old Man's A Dustman'

Having gone through the jazz scene, skiffle stardom, the Variety stage and the cabaret circuit, Lonnie Donegan in his sixties is once again playing the local folk and blues clubs where he is truly appreciated

(the first British record to enter the chart at No. 1). His version of the novelty song 'Does your Chewing Gum Lose its Flavour (On The Bed Post Overnight)', recorded in the late 1950s, gave him his second US Top 10 entry in 1961, making him the most successful British performer of that era in America. Donegan specialised in transforming traditional folk and blues melodies into the skiffle idiom by utilising arrangements that would not have been out of place on rock records. He rarely resorted to covering current US hits, and when he did, as in the case of 'Tom Dooley',' The Battle Of New Orleans' and 'Michael Row The Boat', he never aped the American versions but gave each song his own original up-tempo treatments. Many of the top British acts of the 1960s openly credit Donegan with arousing their interest in music, and others thanked him for giving them the idea of forming a group rather than trying to be a solo artist. He remains both a unique performer and arguably the most important and influential UK artist of the pre-Beatle rock era.

VIPERS

Formed in September 1956, The Vipers quickly landed themselves a twice-weekly residency at London's famous 2 I's coffee house. The group were led by singer/guitarist Walt (later known as Wally) Whyton and included guitarists Johnny Martin (who was also a coffee house manager) and Jean Van Der Bosch, bassist Tony Tolhurst and washboard player John Pilgrim. They soon came to the attention of Parlophone's George Martin, who produced their first release, 'Ain't You Glad'/'Pick A Bale of Cotton' in 1956 (the latter beccoming a hit for Lonnie Donegan in 1962), which was a near hit. Many critics thought that Lonnie Donegan would be the only skiffle act to chart, but success came to The Vipers by dint of their follow-up, the first song ever written by Whyton, 'Don't You Rock Me Daddy-O', which reached the Top 10 (although a cover by Donegan went even higher). Incidentally, at the time of this hit, the group were still only semi-professional, with leader Whyton holding down a worthwhile job in advertising. Their follow-up, an arrangement of the traditional song 'Cumberland Gap', also climbed into the Top 10, but yet again they lost a chart battle with Donegan, whose own version went all the way to No. 1. The group were soon packing venues around the country, scoring major successes at London's Metropolitan and Prince Of Wales Theatres – they made their variety debut at the latter prestigious West End venue in early 1957. Their obligatory train song, 'Streamline Train', cut in May 1957, was to be their last Top 30 entry. Whyton, who was later a noted children's TV presenter, is now the most respected country music DJ in Britain, and has recently been honoured in Nashville for his contribution to the popularisation of country music in Europe.

Despite it being a 'do-it-yourself' craze, the merchandising of skiffle was big business for a short time in the small ads of the music press

CHAS McDEVITT

Chas McDevitt was a guitarist from Glasgow who spent most of his life in the south of England. He started out as a banjo player and in 1956 joined the Crane River Jazz Band (which was formed in 1948 by Ken Colyer) and assembled his own skiffle group within the band. From there, it was on to London's coffee houses and jazz clubs, and before long the group was presenting what McDevitt termed 'skiffle in the raw' at the skiffle-friendly Metropolitan Theatre in London. While they were appearing there their manager Bill Varley (co-writer of 'Don't You Rock Me Daddy-O') added another Glaswegian, folk-singing, one-time busker Nancy Whiskey (born Nancy Wilson) to widen the band's appeal. The group signed to Oriole Records and their first record was a version of the old folk/blues favourite by Elizabeth Cotton, 'Freight Train', which featured Whiskey's distinctive voice and some skiffle whistling from McDevitt. In Britain, helped by its inclusion in the successful film *The Tommy Steele Story*, it became both McDevitt's and Oriole's first hit and spent 17 weeks in the chart, reaching the Top 5 and easily beating a cover version by Bob Cort's Skiffle Group. This new-found success meant that the group were soon seen on British tours supporting visiting American rock acts like Frankie Lymon & The Teenagers and Freddie Bell & The Bellboys. Across the Atlantic, despite losing a chart battle to Rusty Draper's cover version, 'Freight Train' reached the Top 40 and sold over 250,000 copies. Surprisingly, the follow-up, which coupled 'Greenback Dollar' with the equally popular 'I'm Satisfied', only crept into the lower reaches of the UK Top 30. It was not only their last hit but also their final single featuring the distinctive Nancy Whiskey, who had been dubbed 'The First Lady of Skiffle'. Future releases by the group, both with and without their Belfast-born new vocalist, Shirley (Babs) Douglas (who in 1959 became Mrs McDevitt), failed to sustain their popularity. With the proceeds of his successful single, McDevitt opened his own coffee bar, aptly named the Freight Train, in the heart of Soho.

Chas McDevitt behind the Gaggia espresso machine at his Freight Train Coffee Bar which he opened with some of the proceeds from his Top Five hit of the same name

JOHNNY DUNCAN

Duncan, a Tennessee-born singer/guitarist, is reported to have played in blue grass music pioneer Bill Monroe's group, The Blue Grass Boys, in the late 1940s. He was drafted into the US army, stationed in Britain, married an English girl and settled down in the UK after his discharge. In 1956 Duncan replaced banjoist Lonnie Donegan in Chris Barber's Jazzband. In early 1957 he too left Barber and formed his own group, which, somewhat unoriginally, he tagged The Blue Grass Boys. The group, who fused C&W and skiffle, had one major UK hit with their Denis Preston-produced (and Joe Meek-engineered) second single, 'Last Train To San Fernando' (previously recorded by Bobby Short), in 1957. The singer, who was initially billed as 'The Original Rock-a-Billy Kid', also climbed into the Top 30 with follow-ups 'Blue Blue Heartaches' and a credible version of his old boss Bill Monroe's blue grass standard, 'Footprints In The Snow'. Although Duncan was an accomplished C&W performer, don't confuse him with the singer of the same name, who had a string of top country hits in America in the late 1960s and 1970s.

When the army of skiffle strummers went electric, second-hand shops across the country were inundated with cheap acoustic guitars – not to mention rusting washboards

Johnny Duncan – calling his group The Bluegrass Boys hinted at the more country-oriented flavour of his repetoire

Dance On

JIVERS AND TWISTERS

Before World War 2, strict tempo dancing to big bands in the local Palais was how many British people spent their big night out. However, a combination of the austere economics of the postwar years, the reluctance of many battle-weary ex-servicemen to dance daintily round a ballroom, and the public's changing tastes, meant the number of working bands was reduced, and that many of these had to cut back on musicians in order to make a living. Among those that survived and thrived in those first ten years after VE day were bands led by Victor Silvester, Ted Heath, Ken Mackintosh, Joe Loss and Britain's premier exponent of Latin American music, Edmundo Ros.

Rock'n'roll dancing meant a new lease of life to transatlantic jiving and jitterbugging

Dances generally in the early 1950s were still formal occasions. Men wore jackets and ties, the ladies wore dresses - this does not imply that the average man and woman were dressed for *Come Dancing*, but that everyone looked smart. The popular dances of the period included the Quickstep, Foxtrot, Rumba and Tango, all of which had formalised steps that were hard to busk if you didn't know what you were doing. Still, if you had a sympathetic partner and a sense of rhythm, you could bluff your way around the floor by using waltz-steps at the appropriate tempo.

Ballroom dancing was still often a very formal affair; here a deb and her escort make a request to the bandleader at London's Dorchester Hotel

Teddy Boys, who were first seen in London around 1952, had little inclination for ballroom dancing, although many enjoyed the odd rumble at dance halls. If they got on to the floor at all, most of them would simply do the same shuffling steps to a Waltz, Tango or Foxtrot. Band leader Ken Mackintosh overheard someone say to one Teddy

Boy, 'are you dancing or creeping', and this inspired him to write 'The Creep', a record aimed at this section of the younger generation. It gave Mackintosh his biggest hit, and was one of the most covered instrumentals of 1954 in the US (although no versions charted). The dance craze however did not really outlast the sales of the single and future Creep releases (including Mackintosh's 'Creeping Tom') never crept into the chart.

Frenzied teenagers erupting into a 'mass of struggling jivers' was how the newspapers reported this orgy of dancing at a screening of *Rock Around the Clock*

The end of 1954 saw the arrival of North American rock'n'roll and the South American Mambo, with the latter initially wiping the (dance) floor with rock. Before long Rosemary Clooney topped the chart with 'Mambo Italiano' (banned by some US stations for 'not reaching standards of good taste'), Perez Prado and Eddie Calvert both hit No. 1 with 'Cherry Pink', whilst Perry Como ('Papa Loves Mambo') and even Bill Haley ('Mambo Rock') mamboed up the Top 20. America was equally Mambo-mad, and among the interesting US records were Wynonie Harris' (of 'Good Rockin' Tonight' fame) 'Good Mambo Tonight', Bonnie Lou's (the 'Tennessee Wig Walk' hit-maker) 'Tennessee Mambo' and Ruth Brown's R&B chart topper 'Mambo Baby'.

Once Mambo-mania subsided rock'n'roll took over. The Bill Haley film, *Rock Around The Clock*, and the many US movies that quickly followed in its foot-

Pre-rock'n'roll jazz dancing – note the classic 1950s tie!

steps, showed British youngsters how to dance to the music. The impact of these films was such that teenagers would often jive in the cinema aisles, and re-enter the night air 'jitterbugging about'. In one memorable incident, 1,000 hyperactive, jiving teenagers were chased a mile across Liverpool city centre and then dowsed down with fire hoses by police.

Incidentally, in the early and mid-1950s, the actual label credits on many records stated the dance tempo, and when rock first appeared, and record companies were not sure how you danced to it, they put such appellations as 'novelty foxtrot' on the labels.

The music and the dances associated with rock'n'roll soon brought throngs of teenagers into dance halls. Thanks to rock, the dance music business, which was starting to die on its feet, was coming to life again. Jiving as such was nothing new; along with the similarly uninhibited Jitterbug and Lindy-Hop, variations of the Jive had been danced by energetic and extrovert people on both sides of the Atlantic since the 1930s. However, the combination of this relatively unregimented dance and the revolutionary new music swept across British dance halls like a blast of much needed fresh air. Instead of having one foot in the grave, the dance business now had both feet firmly on the dance floor. Most Palais had their own jiving experts, who were as amazingly athletic as any couples seen on films of the time, but the simple basic jive movements were lively and liberated enough for most dancers.

Jiving became more and more extravagant as the decade wore on – here a couple 'cut a rug' in late Fifties New York

The new dance, like the music, was not welcomed with open arms in all quarters. One British clergyman declared, 'Rock'n'roll is a revival of devil dancing, the same sort of thing that is done in black magic rituals. The effect will be to turn young people into devil-worshippers.' Noted band leader and TV music presenter Jack Payne had similar forebodings, but most band leaders gritted their teeth and tried to latch on to the trend as best they could; after all, had not almost the same things been said about the Charleston and Black Bottom in the 1920s, when they were young?

In America, rock'n'roll dancing met with similar resistance, but thanks to TV shows like Dick Clark's *Bandstand*, youthful dance crazes such as the Bop, the Freeze, the Stroll, the Walk, the Shag and the Chalypso (a mix of the Cha Cha and the Calypso) spread from coast to coast in the late 1950s.

Few Britons knew about these dances; they kept up to date by watching UK trend-setters on *6.5 Special* and in 1958 the show launched a revolutionary dance, the Hand Jive. The dance was devised by the clientele of coffee bars which were too small and crowded to allow regular dancing. As the name implies, the Hand Jive is done with the hands and therefore needs no floor space - it can be performed sitting at a table. You simply put one fist on top of another twice, move your hands across each other twice, touch your elbows, do a circle with each hand and start again. Such was the interest that Jack Good wrote an instruction book, *Hand Jive At 6.5*, which included instructions for 'Formation Hand-Jive'. Despite the fact that for a while the Hand Jive kept everyone dancing in their seats, cash-in records by *6.5 Special* regulars Don Lang, Betty Smith and Wee Willie Harris all received the thumbs down from the UK public. In America, R&B star Johnny Otis saw potential in the dance and his composition 'Willie And The Hand Jive' climbed into the US Top 20 in 1958 (making it the only UK dance craze of the 1950s to hit in the States), and charted for Cliff Richard in Britain in 1960. On the subject of Cliff, it seems strange that the nimble footwork displayed by his group, The Shadows, was never turned into a dance - as happened later with the stage routines of acts like Freddie & The Dreamers and The Temptations.

Dancers in the late 1950s also found that variations of the Jive ideally suited both skiffle and trad jazz, and the only new dance many learned

The economical Hand Jive inspired just one memorable piece of music – Johnny Otis' 'Willie And The Hand Jive', covered in the UK by Cliff Richard in 1959 and, more recently, by Eric Clapton

The Twist was truly universal, appealing to all ages and classes; here two socialite Twisters show how its done at London's Satire Club, which was run by one Lord Ulick Browne

was the Cha Cha. In late 1958 it seemed that half the records released had Cha Cha in their titles. However, the only real hit to come from the short-lived craze was the Tommy Dorsey Orchestra's 'Tea For Two Cha Cha'.

The biggest postwar dance, the Twist, was launched in the US in 1960. To twist, all you had to do was 'go round and round and up and down'. You simply pretended you were drying your back with a towel while stubbing out a cigarette with your foot. Even if you couldn't waltz or jive, you could twist, whilst for good dancers there was plenty of opportunity for energetic impro-visations. It was also the first successful dance where you didn't need a part-ner, and if you had one, you didn't touch. This dance, like so many others before and afterwards, was born in black America. Record-wise it started with R&B star Hank Ballard's 'The Twist' in 1959, and when cloned by Chubby Checker, shot to the top of the US chart (it was the only record to reach No. 1 on two separate occasions). Ironically, in Britain the dance was launched in 1962 by Checker's second twist hit, 'Let's Twist Again' (based loosely on Hank Ballard's 'Let's Go Again (Where We Went Last Night)', and by the end of the year literally hundreds of twist records were released. Veteran rock'n'roll and R&B hit-makers saw it as a chance to regain lost popularity, and even the squarest artists, including Frank Sinatra, Victor Silvester and Frankie Vaughan, succeeded in getting older members of the public going 'round and round'.

Checker and his early 1960s US contemporaries also invited us to Hucklebuck, Pony, Fly, Limbo (how low can you go?), Hully Gully, Swim, Watusi, Bristol Stomp, and Mashed Potato, but these dances meant little here. The only ones the British public attempt-ed were the Madison (where you formed a 'big boss line') in 1960 and Little Eva's rock'n'railroad conga, 'The Locomotion' (the dance being invent-ed only after the record hit!), which steamed up the charts in 1962 as The Beatles released 'Love Me Do'. In 1963, not only did the Fab Four help terminate the Twist, they also had the last, and arguably best known Twist hit, with an R&B song previously recorded by The Top Notes/Carla Thomas and The Isley Brothers, 'Twist & Shout'.

Lining up for the Madison, definitely in the Second Division of the dance craze league

Its Trad, Dad

And All That Jazz

Shortly after skiffle had ceased to stimulate British record buyers, its poor relation traditional (trad) jazz, whose roots were also firmly planted in an earlier Afro-American music style, became a major fad.

During World War 2 British musicians like trumpeter Freddy Randall and pianist George Webb were figureheads in the movement that reintroduced the jazz sounds of the past. It was a time when many jazz fans were tiring of glossy swing bands and warmly welcomed the rough and raw approach of these jazz revivalists. The bands they led and later combos like The Crane River Jazz Band (formed by Ken Colyer), Charlie Galbraith's Jazz Band and above all Webb's ex-trumpeter Humphrey Lyttelton's Jazz Band initially helped to popularise the music that had been born in New Orleans in the first decade of the century. These British jazz players had taken their inspiration from many of the great American jazz musicians of the past, including cornet players King Oliver, Bunk Johnson and, most importantly, Louis Armstrong, clarinettists Johnny Dodds and Jimmy Noone, trombonist Kid Ory and pianist Jelly Roll Morton.

A founding figure in the British traditional jazz movement, Humphrey Lyttelton had a hit single in the charts and even a club named after him in London's Oxford Street

By 1953 the demand for their music was great enough for British jazz players like Lyttelton and trombonist Chris Barber to become full-time professional musicians. In seeking to define the music's attraction Barber insisted:'Trad jazz is a very straightforward, easy listenable form of music that anyone can enjoy. There's nothing complex or contrived about it, and unlike so much modern jazz, you don't have to dig down deep to find out what it's all about. After hearing the involved style of jazz played by Stan Kenton and the boppers, the public began looking around for something more simple. They found traditional jazz, and liked it.'

Chris Barber recorded his famous New Orleans Joys album (which included Lonnie Donegan's 'Rock Island Line') in 1954 and explained his band's varied repertoire by saying ,'we don't just play material in the strict New Orleans tradition, we also play rags, blues and even pop songs in the trad jazz idiom', but insisted, 'we don't water down or commercialise the music.'

In the mid-1950s it was British modern jazz, as played by the likes of Ronnie Scott and Johnny Dankworth, that earned most of the headlines; but, to the surprise of many, both Donegan (whose first press article was headed 'Trad Man Makes Top 20') and Lyttelton had taken singles into the charts in 1956. Lyttelton said of his record 'Bad Penny Blues', 'If its success persuaded people to like jazz and to buy the records of some of the great players, I'd say it would be a very good thing indeed.' 1956 also saw the arrival in Britain of the best loved New Orleans jazzman, Louis Armstrong. The Musicians Union exchange deal meant that Armstrong's UK visit enabled Freddy Randall to take his Dixieland band to the US, where they somehow found themselves on the Biggest Rock'n'Roll Show of 1956, playing on the same bill as rock'n'roll pioneers Bill Haley, Frankie Lymon & The Teenagers, The Platters, Joe Turner, Bo Diddley, The Flamingos and The Drifters. Although musically they were as out of place as Cliff Richard on an all-rap bill, they were well received by the 7,000-15,000 teenagers at every show. Incidentally, on his return Randall remarked, 'At some shows down in Dixieland, there were problems with pickets who carried banners urging teenagers not to listen to "jungle music"!'.

Trad jazz clubs were nothing if not informal. Here the fans sit it out on the floor at an 'All Night Jam Session' at the Delta River Jazz Club , Old Compton Street, Soho, in 1951

Just when it looked as if trad was about to make a real commercial breakthrough, its amateurish-sounding offshoot, skiffle, came out like a runaway train, and for a while there wasn't room on the track for both of them. Trad acts had to wait in the sidings, take the odd ride on the *6.5 Special*, and be patient until those tea-chest totin' skif-flers had run out of steam.

However, by 1959 trad was again the most popular music in cellar clubs and at art college 'raves', where tight-jean-clad, baggy-jumper-wearing would-be beatniks danced the night away. In January, the Chris Barber Band's recording of Sidney Bechet's 'Petite Fleur' (featuring clarinettist Monty Sunshine) was flowering into an American Top 10 hit, and shortly afterwards it repeated that journey in Britain. Barber's band soon found themselves in the midst of a North American tour (a case of 'taking trad to New Orleans') during which they appeared on Ed Sullivan's TV show, and received their gold record on the *Hit Parade* television programme. The *New York Times* reviewed their live show enthusiastically, stating, 'they are defi-nitely superior to any equivalent band in America.' The demand for them across the Atlantic meant that New Orleans jazz great, clarinettist George Lewis, found himself

From genuine cult status in the early Fifties, trad went into the pop charts, then reassumed its position in the pub-based jazz circuit where it still flourishes today

back in Britain (in exchange for Chris Barber), playing to enthusiastic crowds and helping to spread the gospel of trad music. A month later Louis 'Satchmo' Armstrong returned to these shores and later in the year the legendary Kid Ory, master of the New Orleans 'tailgate' trombone style, made his UK debut.

The colourful British clarinettist Acker Bilk came to national prominence in early 1960 with his memorable instrumental, 'Summer Set'. The song, whose title was a play on words on Somerset, the county of Bilk's birth, had been written by ex-band member Dave Collett and had started life as a piano solo. Amidst an unprecedented row over Americans too closely cloning British hits (surely a case of the kettle calling the pot black), a cover version of the tune by ex-Paul Whiteman trumpeter Monty Kelly reached the US Top 40 Before the year was out rock music in Britain was visibly suffering under the attack from trad. Even rock's leading impresario Larry Parnes (together will TV producer Jack Good) staged a Rock And Trad tour. Good described the show as 'fast-moving with a pronounced Dixieland theme' and added, 'We're not scrapping rock altogether'. But he refused to say whether he thought the show would have been successful without the association with trad jazz (although in reality the trad input was minimal). The sales of trad albums also skyrocketed in the UK that year, with both Bilk and Barber paying return visits to the Top Twenty.

Acker Bilk established the fad for trad bands to adopt 'character' stage uniforms, as with Dick Charlesworth's City Gents (below)

The first major vocal trad jazz hit was Acker Bilk's version of the Louis Prima favourite 'Buona Sera' at the tail end of 1960, while his treatment of Louis Armstrong's 'That's My Home' followed it into the Top 10 the following year. The next combo to go from cult to commercial status were Kenny Ball & His Jazzmen. The band, who had been taken under Lonnie Donegan's wing, thought their version of '76 Trombones' should be released as a single, but Donegan preferred their lively two-beat version of Cole Porter's song 'Samantha'. He was proved right and the song, from the Hollywood film *High Society*, opened the Ball band's chart account in 1961. The hits continued for Ball, and that year ended with his unlikely version of a Russian song, 'Padmeskoveeye Vietchera', which he titled 'Midnight In Moscow', rushing into the Top 5.

The Temperance Seven, an oddball nine-piece band (they claimed they were often 'one over the eight'), not only played jazz from the 1920s and 1930s but performed it as close as possible to the original version (which included the use of a megaphone for the vocalist), and were attired in the formal evening dress of those past eras. George Martin produced their 1961 debut single, 'You're Driving Me Crazy', which shot them to the top of the UK chart. On the group's instructions, the first pressings of their follow-up, 'Pasadena', were scrapped and they re-recorded it to get a more authentic sound. Their drummer, Professor Brian Innes, was proud to call the finished product 'vastly superior from a musical viewpoint to our first hit.' It also quickly reached the Top 3, but was their last single to do so.

1961 was an interesting year in many ways; it was the year the Berlin Wall was erected, the first year without National Service in the UK and the year when 50,000 CND ('Ban The Bomb') supporters marched (many to the sound of trad bands) from Aldermaston to London. It was also the year when the trad boom reached unprecedented heights. Bilk, Ball, Barber and the Temperance Seven were the top-selling acts, and other bands-in-waiting included those of Terry Lightfoot, Alex Welsh, Dick Charlesworth, ex-Bilk sideman Bob Wallis, Monty Sunshine(who had soloed on 'Petite Fleur'), Micky Ashman, Mick Mulligan and The Clyde Valley Stompers (with Ian Menzies), who were selling goodly amounts of records and attracting big crowds wherever they played. The annual Royal Variety Show was rock-free, but among its headliners were the Dixieland doyens, Kenny Ball and Acker Bilk, and during 1961 Bilk released four Top 20 albums, including two volumes of Best Of Barber & Bilk, on which he and Chris Barber were each featured on one side of a single album.

By April 1961 trad was so popular that *NME* wondered 'Is Trad Killing Rock ?', and asked the music's most popular purveyors, Ball, Barber and Bilk, for their considered opinions. Barber felt the popularity 'was due to its improvisation', explaining that, 'with rock, when a fans sees an act perform, he hears the same thing almost note for note as on the artist's records — which, after a while, loses its appeal, whereas a trad jazz band improvises and the solos are entirely different in most cases.' To emphasise the point, he added: 'Trad bands do more with a tune than rockers,

Along with the All Night Session, the Riverboat Shuffle was one of the institutions of the trad scene – here the fans dance a summer afternoon away on a typical jazz cruise down the Thames

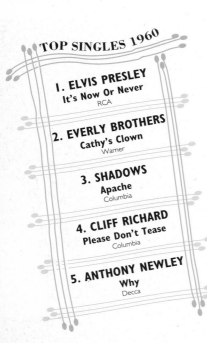

they use the melody simply as a foundation on which to build.' He concluded, 'Trad has as much beat as rock'n'roll, although it's less pronounced, but just as danceable.' Bilk opined, 'Trad bands did not set out to capture pop fans...it just happened, and more and more people are coming around to the trad way of thinking.' The reason, he felt, was that 'Trad is a colourful, exciting, good-time music that makes people want to tap their feet even more than rock'n'roll.' According to Ball, 'Trad has the beat rock fans want, but it's not a forced, over-emphatic beat like rock - swing, I think that's a better word for it'. He added 'Trad is by no means difficult to understand but since it is not as basic as rock it gives the listener more to think about. Noting that jazz clubs had become the social meeting place for young people, he believed, 'One of the major factors in trad's growth is the unashamed enthusiasm of the people who play it.' Ball surmised, 'Trad jazz is not simply a passing craze - it will always be an integral part of the British music scene', adding what in hindsight seems just wishful thinking, 'I feel this present boom will encourage youngsters to take up trad as they did skiffle.'

The dance craze known as the Twist hit Britain in early 1962, and for a while these two strange bedfellows grew and co-existed alongside each other. In March the low-budget movie, *It's Trad, Dad!*, hit Britain's big screens. The film featured hit-makers Ball, Bilk and The Temperance Seven alongside a handful of US rock and pop stars including the twist hit-makers Chubby Checker and Gary 'U.S.' Bonds. As might be expected, musically it fell between too many stools and was not a huge box office success, although the soundtrack album did

British jazz enthusiasts were highly partisan in their taste. Generally trad fans despised modern jazz, and vice versa. Here a group of 'modernists' discuss the latest release by American pianist Dave Brubeck, who was very fashionable at the time

spend 21 weeks on the UK chart and reached the Top 3. As it happened 1962 was to give both Ball and Bilk the biggest hits of their careers. Ball's infectious 'Midnight In Moscow' passed the million sales mark when it took off in the US, only narrowly missing the No. 1 position. Two months later Bilk reached that summit with 'Stranger On The Shore', a record that had already topped the British listings. Ball also added two more UK Top 10 hits to his tally with his energetic and enthusiastic reworkings of Richard Rodgers' show stopper, and now chart topper, 'March Of The Siamese Children' and 'The Green Leaves Of Summer', an Oscar-nominated song from the movie *The Alamo*. Adding icing to his cake was the fact that both these singles entered the US charts, albeit in comparatively lowly positions.

While The Beatles' 'Love Me Do' was awaiting release, Ball and Bilk clocked up a further Top 20 hit apiece with the old Bing Crosby favourite 'So Do I' and the self-composed 'Lonely' respectively. However trad did not survive the Merseyside invasion of the charts for long. In 1963 Ball and Bilk had just one Top 20 single apiece and a couple of chart albums (including the budget-priced The Best of Ball, Barber & Bilk, the only trad LP to ever top the chart) - and from that time onwards trad artists were strangers to the chart.

Trombonist and trad populariser Chris Barber on stage at London's Marquee Club, which before evolving into a premier rock venue in the Sixties was a major jazz club under the auspices of the National Jazz Federation

CHRIS BARBER

Trombonist Barber was born in Welwyn Garden City, Herts., and as a teenager played in the bands of Doug Whitton and Cy Laurie. He formed his first band in 1949, and apart from a short time with Ken Colyer in the early 1950s, has fronted his own outfit ever since. Barber's singles and albums in the 1950s may not have always charted, but the proof that they sold well can be ascertained by the fact that his band released 11 LPs before the end of the decade. Barber described his music as 'happy down-to-earth and unpretentious', adding, 'even the must unmusical people can tap their feet to it .' It was Barber's band that introduced skiffle to the world when they recorded 'Rock Island Line' (featuring their banjo player Lonnie Donegan) in 1954. Donegan's replacement, American Johnny Duncan, also left to find fame (albeit brief in his case) as a semi-skiffle exponent in 1957. The Barber outfit, who had been voted Top Trad Band in the NME poll from 1956-59, had a belated hit of their own in 1959. This time, however, it was the turn of clarinetist

Monty Sunshine to step into the spotlight, when the band's 1956 recording of 'Petite Fleur', taken from the Chris Barber Plays Vol. 3 album, became a transatlantic Top 10 hit. In the US, his recording of this composition by New Orleans legend Sidney Bechet out-pointed covers from top jazzmen Benny Goodman, Woody Herman and Bob Crosby, and Barber was pleased that Bechet lived long enough to see the success. Oddly, Barber did not appear on the A-side of his band's biggest hit and only played bass on the B-side, 'Wild Cat Blues', a 1955 recording which also featured Donegan on banjo. Barber's band with his vocalist wife Ottilie Patterson twice toured the US in 1959 when they were seen on top TV shows and at the Monterey Jazz festival. It was to be the only major hit single for the band who made few concessions to contemporary commercial taste. They have, however, maintained a high performing and recording profile ever since, and their 1980s work with noted New Orleans singer/pianist Dr. John proved very popular in America. Barber, who brought to Britain such legendary musical figures as R&B greats Muddy Waters and Louis Jordan, blues stars Sonny Terry & Brownie McGhee and gospel giants Alex Bradford and Sister Rosetta Tharpe, was a seminal figure in the trad, skiffle and R&B movements in Britain.

ACKER BILK

The bowler-hatted 'Mr' Acker Bilk and his Jazzmen entertaining a capacity crowd at the height of their trad-boom popularity

Somerset-born clarinettist Acker (Bernard) Bilk was the best-known personality in the UK trad jazz boom. He learned his instrument in the late 1940s while serving time (for falling asleep on duty) in an Army prison in Egypt. Bilk played in various outfits in the Bristol area before joining Ken Colyer's Band in 1954. In 1958 he left jazz purist Colyer, added 'Mr.' to his name ('Acker', incidentally is a West Country term for mate or friend) and formed the entertaining Paramount Jazz Band, whose gimmicky Edwardian stage clothes upset jazz purists. Bilk, a singer in the tradition of the two Louis (Armstrong and Prima), had Top 10 entries with 'Summer Set', 'Buona Sera' and 'That's My Home' before scoring his biggest hit in 1961 with a haunting instrumental he had composed under the title 'Jenny' (named after his daughter). The track, which also featured the Leon Young String Chorale, was renamed 'Stranger

On The Shore' when it was used as the theme music to a children's TV series of that name. It not only hit No. 1 in the UK. It stayed on the chart for over a year. Thanks to its chart-topping feat across the Atlantic, Bilk was voted America's Top Instrumentalist Of The Year in 1962, and the haunting single, which had sold more than four million copies around the globe, was voted Top Instrumental Single (it was also a vocal hit in the US for Andy Williams and The Drifters). In 1962 he starred in two films, *Band of Thieves* and *It's Trad, Dad!*, and spent longer on the UK singles chart than any other artist. The ex-blacksmith, who forged a chain of eight Top 30 singles in 1960-3, was trad's No. 1 showman. It was the bearded, bowler-hatted Bilk with his fancy waistcoats who made trad fun and helped the general public acquire a taste for it. He has continued to keep a full working schedule ever since and even briefly returned to the Top 5 of the UK singles and album charts in the late 1970s.

KENNY BALL

Kenny Ball, a trumpet player in the Louis Armstrong tradition, had the biggest run of chart hits of all of the '3 Bs' of trad, Ball, Barber and Bilk

The trumpet-toting band leader from Essex, who was a leading light in the British trad jazz movement, started his career with Charlie Galbraith's All Star Jazz band in 1951. He was later in the bands of Sid Phillips (where he first started singing), drummer Eric Delaney and Terry Lightfoot. He left the latter combo because he wanted to play in a Dixieland fashion, whereas Lightfoot preferred to continue playing in his less raucous New Orleans style. With his band, known as the Chicagoans, Ball played many local gigs in the mid-1950s, and in 1958 formed Kenny Ball & His Jazzmen. He was spotted by Lonnie Donegan who introduced him to Pye Records (for which Donegan himself recorded), who signed the band and placed them with Donegan's producer, Alan A. Freeman. The Ball band were often guests on Donegan's TV series, *Putting On The Donegan*, became regulars on the top-rated BBC radio show *Easy Beat*, and also played long seasons at Frankfurt's well-known Storyville jazz club in 1959 and 1960. Ball's first single for Pye, 'Teddy Bear's Picnic', sold well without charting, as did his debut album, Invitation To The Ball, and the follow up LP with Gary Miller, Gary On The Ball. The band's second single, 'Samantha', was the first of their 13 Top 30 hits, the most successful of which was the Transatlantic Top 5 entry, 'Midnight In Moscow', in 1961 (in the US it easily overcame a cover by notable jazz musician Teddy Buckner). In 1963 Ball, who was criticised by British jazz purists for his Dixieland versions of pop songs, was justifiably proud to become the first British musician to be made an honorary citizen of New Orleans, the birth-place of jazz.

TEMPERANCE SEVEN

This zany band was originally formed in late 1955 at the Royal College of Art. Their music, which was both witty and sophisticated, closely cloned the sounds of the late 1920s & 1930s jazz bands, and their stage wear was the epitome of Edwardian sartorial elegance. The band's musical director was Captain Cephas Howard, who claimed to be the holder of a military award called the Charing Cross, and it featured the (megaphone) vocals of Mr. Paul MacDowell. The personnel also included John R.T. Davies (later well known as a recording engineer). Among the instruments the band featured were pedal clarinet, swanee whistle, phonofiddle, euphonium, harmonium and sousaphone. Before recording in their own right, they backed Peter Sellers on the Peter & Sophia album which the comedian recorded with Sophia Loren. Their debut single, 'You're Driving Me Crazy', originally popularised in 1930 by Guy Lombardo & his Royal Canadians, reached No. 1. All their major successes came in 1961, when they had four Top 20 singles and two Top 20 albums.

According to their drummer, Professor Brian Innes, 'We are very serious about all this, we have a genuine affection not only for the kind of music but also for the style of dress and the period from which it is derived.'

The Temperence Seven were part of an eccentric fringe of musicians that also produced the Massed Alberts and, in later years, the Bonzo Dog Doo Dah Band and Bob Kerr's Whoopee Band

ROCK ON THE SILVER SCREEN

Early rock'n'roll films will never make the lists of all time great movies. As a rule they were cheaply made (and looked it), with story-lines that would not tax a two-year-old. That said, most rock fans in those days when television was still in its infancy, were happy to put up with these shortcomings for the chance of seeing their favourite acts on the silver screen.

It's easy to knock the makers of these films for trying to make a fast buck from rock, but it's not hard to understand why they cut corners. Making movies, unlike making records, was, and still is, very expensive and relatively slow. Investing in a movie about a teenage musical craze was strictly for the 'crazies' and real gamblers only. Teen tastes changed fast, and no one sells less cinema seats than a pop has-been. Owing to the very nature of the business, even when film companies worked at full speed, a movie usually took several months to reach the screen, and such delays could prove financially disastrous.

Front-of-house still for a typical American rock'n'roll exploiter, *Shake Rattle and Rock*

Amazingly, it was this delay that led to the initial world-wide success of rock'n'roll. In 1954, MGM wanted a record to include in *The Blackboard Jungle*, a Glenn Ford movie about rebellious teenagers in an American high school. They selected, 'Rock Around The Clock', a recent release by the up-and-coming Bill Haley & The Comets. However, by the time the film surfaced, almost a year later, that record had stiffed, but the group had released a further three singles. Luckily, all of them had hit the US Top 20, and Haley's outfit were now one of the country's hottest properties. Subsequently, when Haley's old record was re-issued, it quickly followed his previous big hits into the chart, and its huge US success helped launch it internationally.

The film's impact was so great that Haley was soon starring in the first rock'n'roll musical, also entitled *Rock Around The Clock*. *The Blackboard Jungle* linked juvenile delinquency to r'n'r; hence, virtually all US and British rock films began with a conflict between the generations and ended with the authorities being converted to the music.

In Britain, the US rock'n'roll movies were received like manna from heaven by rock-starved fans, although the majority would have been more than content to skip the corny story lines and simply have non-stop music (film makers did not realise this obvious fact until *Woodstock* in 1970). Stand-outs amongst the early US r'n'r movies must be *Rock Around The Clock*, *Don't Knock The Rock*, the R&B oriented *Mr. Rock & Roll*, *The Girl Can't Help It* (whose budget actually stretched to colour!) and Elvis' *Loving You*, *Jailhouse Rock* and *King Creole*. Colonel Tom Parker may have screwed up Presley's later film career, but his first few films are among the better examples of rock on celluloid.

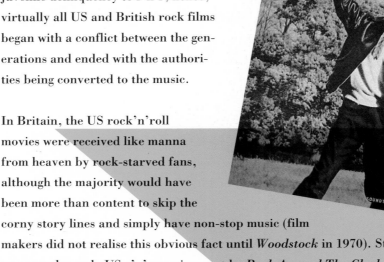

The soundtrack album from Tommy Steele's second cinema epic *The Duke Wore Jeans*

The earliest rock'n'roll superstar, Bill Haley, was also the first to make it on the big screen

Britain's first 'answer to Elvis', Tommy Steele, who had played a cameo role as a coffee bar singer in the film *Kill Me Tomorrow*, had been in show business only a couple of months when, in 1957, he starred in his own bio-pic, *The Tommy Steele Story*. The posters read 'The TRUE story of Britain's most sensational entertainer', but the story line was part truth, part fiction and entirely an excuse for the cheerful cockney to sing and smile a lot. Songwriter Lionel Bart recalled, ' The film company required 16 songs, and insisted that they were not all rock'n'roll, they wanted Cockney songs and calypsos, and said I had to write one called "A Handful Of Songs" - it was one of

Marty Wilde (far left)
and Joe Brown (far right)
featured in the early
Sixties comedy *What a
Crazy World* that also
cameoed beat group
Freddie and the
Dreamers

Steele's biggest hits.' The film itself broke box-office records in Great Britain and the sound-track album – unusually for a rock movie – also sold extremely well.

Steele followed his success by playing two roles - both smiling - in *The Duke Wore Jeans* in 1958, but many fans felt he betrayed rock with his 1959 film *Tommy the Toreador*, which included the novelty, 'Little White Bull', which was closer in style to George Formby than Elvis. It was incidentally the first film ever to receive a Royal premiere in the East End of London.

· The first UK production in the style of *The Girl Can't Help It* was *6.5 Special* in 1957, based on the BBC-TV series. Two young adolescents, chosen for audience identification, board a train and – would you believe – their fellow passengers are popular stars including Jim Dale, Lonnie Donegan (who later appeared in the film *Light Fingers*), Petula Clark, Russ Hamilton, Jackie Dennis, The John Barry Seven (Barry's later film work earned him Oscars) and The King Brothers, whose Denis King recalled: 'We only did one day on the film and mimed two songs. The film was embarrassing; the soundtrack was out of sync'. The film also included spots by Joan Regan and Dickie Valentine, which brings us to the subject of the 'token MOR act'. Movie-makers were under the misapprehension that if they added such acts, they would increase their potential audience. However, in practice, these

The John Barry Seven
were among the
'fabulous array of stars'
appearing in *6.5 Special*

'square' acts stood out like Wee Willie Harris in a convent, and their loyal fans would no more watch a film like *6.5 Special* than throw themselves under the train it was supposedly filmed on.

Also in 1957, a 59-minute British cheapie, *Rock You Sinners*, was rush released. Its stars included Jackie Collins, sister of film star Joan (and now a best-selling novelist), and featured jazz musicians turned rockers Art Baxter & His Rockin' Sinners, Tony Crombie & His Rockets, and the even more obscure Don Sollash & His Rockin' Horses.

In the 1957 popularity poll in *Picturegoer*, the British movie magazine, the award for Top Screen Singing Star went to Liverpool's Frankie Vaughan (Pat Boone was second and Elvis third). Pin-up boy Vaughan was mobbed by screaming fans at the London premiere of *These Dangerous Years*, a film about a teenage gang leader who ends up on the straight-and-narrow. Vaughan's film career continued with *Wonderful Things* and *The Lady Is A Square* (which co-starred Anna Neagle) and in 1960 came that famed head-line, 'Frankie Goes To Hollywood'. His trip resulted in the filming of *Let's Make Love* with Yves Montand and Marilyn Monroe, but although he received good notices, it did not lead to a lucrative movie career.

Russ Hamilton in a scene from the television spin-off movie *6.5 Special*

The first UK rock'n'roll film of 1958 starred Britain's second 'answer to Elvis', Terry Dene, playing a coffee bar singer who becomes a star – where did they dream up these complex plots? – in *The Golden Disc*. Instead of his hits, the amiable Dene sang a handful of pleasant but instantly forgettable songs, and the film also managed to squeeze in cameo appearances from skif-flers Nancy Whiskey, Les Hobeaux and Sonny Stewart's Skiffle Kings, not forgetting the token middle-of-the-road performer, Dennis Lotis.

1959 was a better year for British musicals. The most successful were the humorous rock'n'roll parody *Idle On Parade*, starring Anthony Newley (who also appeared in the film *Jazzboat*), and Cliff Richard's first films, the X-rated *Serious Charge* (the serious charge in question being a vicar's alleged homosexual assault on Cliff) and *Expresso Bongo*. The latter film starred Laurence Harvey as a theatrical agent determined to make a star out of Bongo Herbert(!), a Soho coffee bar singer (another ingenious plot). Incidentally, the youthful Cliff (Herbert) had to have false hair stuck on his chest in a semi-naked scene. Not surprisingly, Cliff is better remembered for *The Young Ones* (1961), in which he saves a youth club and convinces his property developer father, Robert Morley, that rock'n'roll is worthwhile. It was the anglicised version of the standard US rock movie plot, and included that classic (and oft-used) line, 'Let's do the show right here'. Both the film and the soundtrack album were enormously successful, even though much of the score, like that for *Expresso Bongo*, was straight show-biz.

Cliff's main rival in the early 1960s, hollow-cheeked Adam Faith, started with a couple of dramatic roles. He played a beatnik in *Beat Girl* and a petty thief in *Never Let Go*, in which, not surprisingly, he was upstaged by Peter Sellers. His third film, *What a Whopper*(1961), a forgettable comedy about the Loch Ness monster, was followed by *Mix Me A Person*, in which he was under threat of the death penalty.

On a lighter note, in 1962 British group The Eagles appeared with Kenneth More in *Some People*, about a group of teenagers who become model citizens. In the same year film posters proclaimed, 'The screen sizzles when Billy Fury, Helen Shapiro and Bobby Vee Play It Cool'. But *Play It Cool* (1962), which also featured Danny Williams and Shane Fenton , turned out to be a damp squib.

Despite being a 'serious' movie, the Cliff Richard film *Serious Charge* was still promoted on rock'n'roll teen appeal

Vox Pops

The Groups

In the 1950s groups were as much a part of the US rock'n'roll scene as solo artists. Literally thousands recorded during the decade and hundreds charted - it was truly the golden age of American groups.

Things could not have been more different on this side of the Atlantic - British rock'n'roll groups were as rare as Elvis Presley flops. As 1955 dawned *NME* readers voted The Stargazers, The Coronets and The Keynotes Top British Vocal Groups, and such middle-of-the-road stalwarts as the Beverley Sisters and the Johnston Brothers were also resident in the Top 10. Twelve months later, when 'Rock Around The Clock' topped the charts, the poll results were almost identical, and a year after that, despite 12 months of heavy bombardment from the big guns of rock, those five acts were still hogging the top rungs. If you exclude The Hedley Ward Trio (who were occasionally known to get the odd foot tapping) not a single rock-related group appeared in the Top Ten places of the poll!

The cutesie-pie Beverley Sisters lasted longer than any of their rivals, and even enjoyed a late-Eighties revival as a raunchy cabaret act. The King Brothers, on the other hand, faded from view with the end of the Fifties

The only vocal groups to top the UK chart in the 1950s were mixed quintet the Stargazers (with spirited cover versions of the Mariners' novelty, 'I See The Moon', and Art & Dotty Todd's 'Broken Wings'), and the Johnston Brothers (with their interpretation of Archie Bleyer's US hit, 'Hernando's Hideaway'). Both groups achieved this feat before the arrival of rock'n'roll and they were well past their sell-by dates when the decade ended.

Apart from skiffle groups, 1957 saw the emergence of the talented, though decidedly dated, teenage trio, The King Brothers, as Britain's leading group. Being mistakenly dubbed 'Britain's Rock'n'Roll Kids' annoyed the group. Mike King said in 1960, 'Frankly, rock'n'roll isn't our cup of tea – we did a little rock once in a while but we never really were a rock unit, and we're glad we've got away from the tag now.' Thanks in part to their regular

TV appearances they had several chart entries, including their treatment of 'A White Sport Coat' in 1957 and the bouncy show songs 'Standing On The Corner' and '76 Trombones', in the early 1960s. The fact that they were still considered one of Britain's top groups when their Parlophone label mates, The Beatles, arrived on the scene, is less an indication of their popularity than proof of how little competition existed in this field in Britain at the time.

The only other local vocal teams to reach the UK Top 20 in the late 1950s were The Southlanders, the Beverley Sisters, the Kaye Sisters and mixed trios The Mudlarks and The Avons. The Kayes, who were cast from the same mould as the Beverley Sisters, are best remembered for their UK-targeted version of Anita Bryant's weepie, 'Paper Roses', in 1960. The Mudlarks scored their two biggest hits with the novelty pop rockers, 'Lollipop' and 'Book Of Love', which had been Top 10 US records for The Chordettes and The Monotones (who wrote the 'Book Of Love'!) respectively, and the sole Top 20 excursion for The Avons came with their interpretation of Paul Evans' catchy American hit, 'Seven Little Girls Sitting In The Back Seat'. As readers have probably noticed, the common link between all the successful UK vocal groups of the 1950s, aside from their clean cut images, was their regular reliance on proven US hit songs.

Among the other UK vocal groups who tried without success to sell records to the rock market in the 1950s were the Four Jones Boys, whose 1956 recording of 'Tutti Frutti' was released in the UK before Little Richard's original version, and the Dene Boys, whose recording of 'Bye Bye Love' was no threat to the Everly Brothers' version. Other regular visitors to cover-land but never to the charts were the Lana Sisters (who included a young Dusty Springfield) and the Barry Sisters. Regular TV exposure was not always a passport to the hit parade, as the oft-seen but unconvincing rock group, the Dallas Boys, and the more interesting Neville Taylor & The Cutters will confirm. If you're ever held prisoner by a 1950s British group freak and your life depends on naming some notable UK groups of the decade, you may be spared if you suggest The Kestrels, The Five Chestnuts or The Four Jacks. The Five Chestnuts were a group formed by comedian Charlie Chester's 16-year-old son Peter, and included Hank Marvin and Bruce Welch (whose next gig was in The Drifters/ Shadows). Their recording of 'Teenage Love' in 1958 sounded American,

The Southlanders had just one British hit, 'Alone' which got to Number 17 slot in 1957

The King Brother leapt to national fame with their appearance on the children's television talent show 'All Your Own'

which was the biggest compliment you could pay at the time. The Kestrels (who included Roger Greenaway, later one of Britain's all-time top songwriters, and Tony Burrows , the voice that later launched a thousand groups) were Britain's answer to America's many bird-groups (Orioles, Flamingos, Ravens, etc.), and in an equitable world their Platters-style recordings, including a riveting revival of the 1936 song, 'In The Chapel In The Moonlight', would have been chart toppers. The Four Jacks (not to be confused with the earlier US vocal group) were, as their name suggests, actual sailors, whose recording of 'Prayer Of Love' deserved better than sinking without trace.

Elvis Presley's days as an exclusively teen idol were over by the early Sixties, and the groups gathering in the charts on both sides of the Atlantic were early warning hints of his eventual successors as rock'n'roll supremos

As the 1960s began vocal groups were still in short supply, but in their stead came a growing number of self-contained backing groups. Unlike the UK's first rock bands, most of their members were not jazzers moonlighting for a quick quid, but were the first generation of rock musicians – attracted to the entertainment world by Haley, Presley, Steele and their ilk. In many cases they had cut their musical teeth in one of the thousands of British skiffle ensembles. The first of these to step into the limelight and build their own fan base were Cliff Richard's Shadows. They were by far the most influential and imitated group on the British scene before the arrival of The Beatles, and redefined the public's perception of backing groups. When asked in the early 1960s about their success, Hank Marvin said, 'We always try to start trends rather than follow them. Let people copy us, that's our motto.' Their Shadows Walk became an essential part of every youth club group's stage presentation, and their many foot-tapping instrumental hits were staples in the repertoires of thousands of wanna-sound-alike combos complete with identical Fender guitars and Vox amplifiers. The Shadows were without doubt the most successful British group of the pre-Beatles era yet, despite their enormous popularity in the UK, they have never had an American chart record on their own. Following in their shadows, many other groups of the period were given equal billing with the singer they backed, the best known of these being The Checkmates (Emile Ford), The Bruvvers (Joe Brown), The Pirates (Johnny Kidd), The Wildcats (Marty Wilde), The Bruisers (Tommy Bruce) and The Fentones (Shane Fenton).

Britain's only successful vocal groups in the earliest years of the 1960s were The Vernons Girls, The Viscounts (not to be confused with the New Jersey quintet who recorded 'Harlem Nocturne') and The Springfields. After several unsuccessful singles, The Vernons Girls (whose numerous television appearances had probably made them the most recognised female UK group of the early rock era) had their sole Top 20 entry with 'Lover Please', a song that Clyde McPhatter had earlier taken into the

US Top 10. The Viscounts reached the Top 30 with a cover of Paul Chaplain's revival of the nursery rhyme, 'Short'nin' Bread', in 1960, and a year later they cracked the Top 20 with a novelty doo-wop song previously recorded by its composer Barry Mann, 'Who Put The Bomp'. The most original British vocal group of the pre-Beatles era were arguably the commercial, folk-flavoured trio The Springfields. They were not dyed-in-the-wool folkies and, as lead singer Dusty Springfield explained, they chose their route to success because 'there are very few folk groups on the UK pop scene and the adoption of a folky-spiritual style has enabled us to create a rather distinctive and easily recognisable sound.' The trio, who could always be relied on to serve up their unique vocal harmonies on a platter of interesting and unusual instrumentation, took over as Britain's most popular vocal group - a position they held until the arrival of a certain Liverpool foursome.

Among the lesser known groups at the dawn of the 1960s whose recordings, though not major hits at the time, are now considered by many to be laudable (if not downright applaudable) are The Canons (whose Ramrods' styled rehash of 'I Didn't Know The Gun Was Loaded' was a classic of its kind), The Fleerekkers, The Hunters, The Krew Kats (who evolved from Marty Wilde's Wild Cats), The Packabeats, and Sounds Incorporated, who were later signed by Brian Epstein. Amongst the better-regarded groups who featured a lead performer were Bobby Angelo & The Tuxedos (their 'Baby Sittin'' is thought by many to be a classic British rocker) and Buddy Holly clone Buddy Britten & The Regents. There were also Lee Diamond & The Cherokees ('I'll Step Down' was a high spot of 1961), Peter Jay & The Jay Walkers, the Roman-garbed Nero & The Gladiators, Brian Poole & The Tremeloes (who had a bright future ahead of them), Robb Storme & The Whispers, and Terry White & The Terriers.

Ever since the Everly Brothers had made male rock vocal duos trendy in 1957, Britain had tried to produce a home-grown act to rival them, and early abortive attempts like Bill & Brett Landis or the Most Brothers, who featured a young Mickie Most (one of the most successful producers of the 1960s and 1970s), and Alex Murray (who later produced the Moody Blues debut hit, 'Go Now') did not deter the more ambitious duos. In 1961 it looked as if real competition had been found for Don and Phil in the shape of the Allisons, whose self-composed debut disc, 'Are You Sure', topped the chart and came second in the *Eurovision Song Contest*, selling over a million copies world-wide. However, it seems the duo

The Everly Brothers' unique harmony style had a profound influence on virtually every vocal-based group of the late Fifties and early Sixties

97

had saved the best for first and subsequent records never returned them to the upper reaches of the chart. They were soon replaced in the hearts of British record buyers by another pair heavily influenced by the Everly Brothers, the Brook Brothers. This duo reverted to the time-honoured British practice of covering American songs, although in their case the productions by young A&R man/songwriter Tony Hatch were on a par with the original versions – sending out a warning to the world that Britain was almost ready to take on Uncle Sam at his own game. However, the possibility of beating the Americans in their own backyard still seemed like a pipedream when 1962 dawned.

Successful British vocal groups were so thin on the ground in 1962 that an *NME* headline screamed 'What's Happened To The Vocal Groups ?' After studying chart statistics, journalist Derek Johnson noted:'There has been a considerable decline in the popularity of records by vocal groups; particularly out of favour are our own British teams, and I cannot foresee any immediate improvement in the situation.' This sorry state of affairs was examined in some depth and the conclusions reached included that 'the Kayes, Kings and Mudlarks could be a little outdated, and fans have grown tired of the drawling nasal Everly Brothers approach of the Brooks and The Allisons'. The article pointed out that in America groups had always been more popular than in the UK, suggesting that this was partly due to the success of rhythm & blues (R&B) there. Johnson ended on a bright note saying, 'Hits are on the cards for UK outfits The Kestrels, The Countrymen, The Polka Dots and Carter-Lewis & the Southerners.' In actuality these four groups, who managed only one Top 20 entry between them, were soon consigned to oblivion by the beat groups that followed them.

The first British group to top the US chart was not, as many think, The Beatles, but instrumental combo the Tornados, whose recording of 'Telstar' rocketed them to the No. 1 spot on both sides of the Atlantic in 1962. The UK music industry was used to the occasional 'freak' hit Stateside and therefore was not at all surprised when 'Telstar' failed to make America hungry for Britain's Hit Parade heroes. In 1962, transatlantic stardom was still a one-way street. There was no more interest on the other side of the Atlantic in Britain's mohair-suited early 1960s superstars than there had been in their late 1950's counterparts.

The Allisons' first hit 'Are You Sure' was never matched by their subsequent chart entries, 'Words' and 'Lessons In Love' just scraping into the Top 40 in 1961 and '62

The Tornados 'Telstar' stayed in the charts for an incredible 25 weeks

All in all, Britain's track record for producing great rock groups was still laughable when EMI signed The Beatles in mid-1962. If there was ever to be a real break-through for UK acts in the US (and there was little reason at the time to believe there would be), it seemed obvious to everyone in the British music business that it would come via the country's outstanding solo artists – since Britain, unlike America, was not thought of as a breeding ground for world class groups.

Vocal group The Stargazers were among only twelve acts to have their first two hits make the Number One spot

K I N G   B R O T H E R S

Brothers Michael (guitar), Tony (bass) and Denis (piano) King, who came from Hornchurch, Essex, were one of Britain's top groups in the pre-Beatles era. Denis, the youngest member of this teenage trio, was only 14 when they made their television debut on *Shop Window* in 1953. The group, who were often seen on mid-1950s children's TV programmes, appeared at London's famous Astor and Embassy clubs in 1954, played a season at the notorious Windmill Theatre, and were even seen at the London Palladium in 1955, all of this before any of them was old enough to vote. In 1957, after recording unsuccessfully for World Record Club and Conquest, the youthful-looking (but old-fashioned sound-ing) trio signed to Parlophone. They chart-ed with happy-go-lucky covers of Marty Robbins' 'A White Sport Coat', Tony Bennett's only US Top 10 hit of the rock era, 'In The Middle Of An Island', and even The Everly Brothers' classic 'Wake Up, Little Susie'. The clean-cut crew, who were often voted Britain's Top Vocal Group by readers of the music press, managed three more Top 20s in 1960-1, again with Norman Newell-produced covers of US songs, the biggest of these being 'Standing On The Corner', from the musical *The Most Happy Fella*, which took them into the Top 10 for the second time. The brothers, who were quite open about their dislike of r'n'r, were perhaps lucky to have been in the right place at a time when British audiences were looking for a vocal group of their own, and were equally fortunate in their choice of covers. When they decided to record

The King Brothers in a publicity shot for the cinema version of *6.5 Special* which also starred an array of mid-Fifties pop names from Dickie Valentine to Lonnie Donegan

Almost as familiar as The Beverley Sisters on British television, The Kaye Sisters sported Beatle-style mop-tops way before their time

their own compositions the hits ceased, and when The Beatles redrew the blueprints for British groups they refused to board the band wagon, opting instead for a one-way trip to the valley of forgotten idols. Denis has since become one of the UK's most successful music writers for TV, penning the themes for *Bouquet of Barbed Wire*, *Fenn St. Gang*, *Within These Walls*, *Black Beauty* and *Lovejoy* among others.

KAYE SISTERS

This Pop trio comprised Sheila Jones from London, Shirley (Shan) Palmer from Hull and Carole Young from Oldham. It was formed in 1954 by Carmen Kaye and originally known as the Three Kayes. Their big break came when they appeared on TV's *In Town Tonight* in 1956, which led to a fortnight at the London Palladium and a chart hit with a cover of Cathy Carr's US smash 'Ivory Tower' on HMV. They joined Philips in 1957 and their first two Top 10 hits, on which they sang with Frankie Vaughan, were timely covers of Bob Jaxon's humorous 'Gotta Have Something In The Bank Frank' (their royalties for this novelty hit went to Vaughan's pet charity, the Boys Clubs) and the Fleetwoods' haunting American chart-topper, 'Come Softly To Me'. Of the many singles they released alone, their only Top 10 entry was 'Paper Roses' in 1960. They remained a popular attraction on the cabaret circuit long after their hits dried up.

Mr and Mrs Mudd's little Mudds, known as The Mudlarks, one of the top British vocal acts of the late Fifties

MUDLARKS

Soprano Mary Mudd, baritone Fred Mudd and tenor Jeff Mudd were the Mudlarks, a clean-cut family pop act from Bedford. They started singing in public as the Mudd Trio in 1951 when aged 12, 14 and 16 respectively. Top DJ David Jacobs brought them to the attention of ace producer Norrie Paramor, who signed them to Columbia Records. Their second single, 'Lollipop', hit the UK Top Ten, as did the follow-up, a chirpy cover of 'Book Of Love'. The lively trio, who were often seen on TV and were regular guests on *6.5 Special*, won the *NME* poll award as Top British Vocal Group for both 1958 and 1959. Jeff was called up for National Service in early 1959 and David Lane replaced him until his return two years later. The public's interest in their records had waned by 1959 and a string of subsequent singles stiffed for the trio, whose name is inscribed in the 'Book Of 1950s Has-Beens'.

AVONS

Not to be confused with any of the US groups of the same name, the British Avons were Valerie Murtagh (from London), her sister-in-law Elaine Murtagh (from County Cork, Ireland) and Ray Adams. The two girls signed to Columbia Records as the Avon Sisters in 1958, after being discovered singing at the Radio Exhibition. Their first release was 'Which Witch Doctor' with the Mudlarks, and their debut solo single was a cover of The Flamingos' 'Jerri Lee' — both of which stalled outside the chart. They became The Avons with the addition of Ray Adams (from Jersey), whom they had spotted singing with Nat Gonella's Band. Their first release under the new name, 'Seven Little Girls Sitting In The Back Seat' in 1959, was their only UK Top 20 entry. The pop trio also had minor hits with their version of Brian Hyland's 'Four Little Heels' in 1960 and with a bouncy cover of Bobby Vee's 'Rubber Ball' the following year. In 1962 The Shadows' recording of the trio's composition 'Dance On' topped the UK charts, and a year later a vocal version by Kathy Kirby quickly reintroduced their song to the Hit Parade. The Avons themselves label-hopped in the 1960s but their own later recordings failed to make any chart headway. Valerie Avon (as she was then known) continued to have success as a writer, and is still a well-known behind-the-scenes figure in the UK music business.

Here pictured in 1960, the Avons' image already seemed well outdated

SHADOWS

The Shadows are the biggest-selling instrumental act of all time in the UK and the group with the longest span of chart hits. Originally known as The Drifters, they were formed as the backing band for Cliff Richard, and had several personnel changes before settling in late 1958 on the line-up of Hank Marvin (lead guitar), Bruce Welch (rhythm guitar), Terence 'Jet' Harris (bass) and Tony Meehan (drums). Ex-member Ian Samwell, who had penned Cliff's debut single 'Move It', also wrote the group's first release, 'Feelin' Fine'. When this vocal track failed to cross counters they released an instrumental composed by Harris, 'Jet Black' (issued in the States under the name the Four Jets), which again received little radio support and also stayed on record shop shelves. It was not even third time lucky for the high profile group, as sales of their first release as The Shadows, a catchy vocal 'Saturday Dance', penned by Marvin and his ex-boss Peter Chester, of the Five

101

The Shadows (above) were a seminal influence on groups to come, while the Vernons Girls were very much of the time

Chesternuts, completed their hat-trick of near misses. In early 1960, after returning from a US tour with Cliff, they recorded a Jerry Lordan composition 'Apache', originally cut a couple of months earlier by guitarist Bert Weedon for his album King Size Guitar. Their producer Norrie Paramor originally felt it should be the B-side, but after getting his daughter's reactions agreed with the group. Cliff played bongos on their version, which topped the UK chart for six weeks, and the following year a cover by Danish guitarist Jorgen Ingmann narrowly missed the top of the US chart, with both hit versions going on to sell over a million copies world-wide. In November 1960, with the *NME* Poll award for Top British Small Group on their mantelpiece, they released their very different follow-up 'Man Of Mystery', on which Marvin played everything on the treble strings. This also reached the Top 10, as did the their next 10 singles. Bruce Welch said of their hits, 'If you analyse them, you'll find we always have the same basic sound. It's just that we continually vary the tempo and rhythm'. In 1961 they not only became the first group to top the UK Album chart but their eponymous debut album was also the first LP by any British artist to reach No. 1. In October 1961 Meehan left, and six months later Harris went solo. It was not long before Harris had chalked up a couple of medium-sized hits, and when he teamed with Meehan in 1963, the instrumental duo quickly accumulated three Top 10 entries. The Shadows' only other chart-topping single in the pre-Beatles era came in early 1962 with another Jerry Lordan composition, 'Wonderful Land', which held off all competition for two months. They said about it, 'We had originally recorded it over a year earlier but were not happy with it until EMI overdubbed strings. We could not attend the string session ourselves, so Cliff oversaw it.' In their long and very successful career they have put 25 sides into the UK Top 20 (many being self-composed) and 17 of their albums have similarly scored on the LP chart, a figure which is still increasing. The Shadows were genuine innovators whose importance and influence on the UK music scene cannot be overstated.

V E R N O N S   G I R L S

The Vernons Girls, who were sponsored by Vernons, the Liverpool-based football pools company, started out as a 70-strong choir singing songs like 'Nymphs and Shepherds'. The line-up was reduced to 16 by the late 1950s, when they were regularly seen on the top-rated pop TV show *Oh Boy!* This large ensemble recorded without success for Parlophone in 1958-61. In 1962, when the group had been reduced to the trio of Maureen Kennedy, Jean Owen and Frances Lee, they had their sole best-seller, 'Lover Please'. Its B-side, a novelty song, 'You Know What I Mean', also hit the lower regions of the chart, as did later covers of Little Eva's 'Loco-Motion', Dee Dee Sharp's 'Do The Bird' and the original song 'Funny All Over'. The Vernons Girls group of the 1950s also spawned solo chart artist Lynn Cornell and the well-known session vocal groups The Ladybirds, The Breakaways and The Two-Tones. With often changing personnel, the group maintained a performing profile for many years.

The Vernons Girls' 'You Know What I Mean' was an early example of the Liverpool 'Scouse' accent in British pop

SPRINGFIELDS

The Springfields epitomised a fresh-sounding pop that heralded the folk-rock sound that was to come out of America not long after

When Londoners Tom Springfield (Dion O'Brien) and Tim Feild (sic) added Tom's sister Dusty (Mary O'Brien) to their folk act in mid-1960, they renamed themselves The Springfields (reputedly because they rehearsed in fields on spring days!). The trio, who sang in nine languages and whose repertoire included folk songs from all around the world, were one of the most original and innovative British acts of the 1960s. Dusty said, 'We're not what you might call authentic folk singers. Ours is a slightly commercial approach to folk music, because in this way we hope to win the acceptance of the public as a whole and not just a minority section.' Their first release, 'Dear John', in 1961, came like a much-needed breath of fresh air to the UK music scene, and the trio soon scored their first Top 20 entry with 'Bambino', a 250 - year-old Neapolitan carol with English lyrics written by Tom. Such was their impact that they were voted Top UK Vocal Group in the *NME* poll in 1961, and in 1962, after Mike Hurst (Mike Longhurst-Pickworth) replaced Feild, the trio again collected that coveted award. Among their most memorable records were their 1963 Top 10 hits 'Island Of Dreams' and 'Say I Won't Be There', while 'Silver Threads And Golden Needles' climbed into the US Top 20 (at the time that The Beatles released 'Love Me Do'), and entered the Australian Top 15 at No. 1. The trio, who in 1962 were voted among the 10 Most Promising Groups in the US, appeared in the all-star UK film *Just For Fun*, before deciding in 1963 to split while they were still at the top. All three members continued to notch up record business successes. Tom wrote big hits for acts like The Seekers,

Hurst produced many chart records for Cat Stevens, Showaddywaddy and Shakin' Stevens, and Dusty left folk music behind, discovered mascara and went on to become one of the world's top-selling female artists in the 1960s.

ALLISONS

Although the Allisons were initially touted as England's answer to the Everly Brothers, their main claim to fame was their almost winning the Eurovision Song Contest

Londoner John Alford and Bob Day from Wiltshire formed pop duo The Allisons and played the rounds of coffee bars and youth clubs before impresario Tito Burns discovered them and became their manager. The supposed brothers became overnight British celebrities when their memorable 'Are You Sure' was selected as Britain's entry in the 1961 *Eurovision Song Contest*. They received the biggest wave of publicity ever afforded unknowns when this undeniably catchy composition became runner-up in the prestigious competition. Produced by Jack Baverstock and arranged by Harry Robinson (of Lord Rockingham's XI fame), 'Are You Sure' went to No. 1 in Britain, sold over a million in Europe and narrowly missed the US chart. Incidentally, the duo were one of many UK acts of the period whose music inspired comparisons with Buddy Holly, with their debut LP containing three songs associated with the late Lubbock legend. Interest in The Allisons cooled quickly and their other chart entries, 'Words' and 'Lessons In Love' (a song from Cliff Richard's film *The Young Ones*), failed to crack the Top 20.

TORNADOS

Music press ads for the Shadows' 'Apache' read 'Hold on to your scalps, here come the Shadows!'

This instrumental group which initially consisted of Alan Caddy (lead guitar), George Bellamy (rhythm guitar), Roger Lavern (keyboards), Heinz Burt (bass) and Clem Cattini (drums), was assembled by the legendary British producer Joe Meek, both as the in-house band for his home studio and as possible rivals to The Shadows. In 1962 they backed John Leyton and Billy Fury on tour, and the latter singer inspired their debut single, 'Love And Fury'. Their perennial calling-card, 'Telstar', was written as a tribute to the Telstar communication satellite (launched in July 1962) by ex-TV engineer Meek who was 'absolutely thrilled with the brilliance of the achievement.' The group recorded the track in only 90 minutes and rushed back to Yarmouth just in time to back Fury on stage (before the hit single, they did not even have a spot of their own on the show). By the end of that year 'Telstar' had become a transatlantic No. 1 for this organ-led combo, and had achieved global sales of over five million. Their follow-up, 'Globetrotter', which revisited 'Telstar' terrain, almost returned the quintet to the top in Britain. The team released umpteen variations on a similar theme, with their 1963 releases 'Robot' and 'Ice Cream Man' reaching the Top 20 Best Sellers. The photogenic Heinz Burt struck out on his own in early 1963 and had success commensurate to his vocal talent.

One of the biggest group hits just before the beat era was the 1962 chart topper 'Nut Rocker' by the American B.Bumble and the Stingers

BROOK BROTHERS

Geoffrey and Ricky Brook from Winchester, Hampshire, were often called the 'British Everly Brothers'. They first sang together in a skiffle group in 1956, and started down the road to fame after winning a talent competition on Southern TV's *Home Grown*. In 1960 they joined Top Rank Records and their debut single, 'Greenfields' (a treatment of the Brothers Four's US hit), reportedly sold well in Italy. They followed it with a double-sided cover, coupling Hank Locklin's country song 'Please Help Me I'm Falling' and The Everly Brothers' 'When Will I Be Loved?' When producer Tony Hatch moved to Pye Records, they followed, and

Even more seriously compared to the Everlys, the Brook Brothers were another duo whose hit days were numbered once the guitar-group boom got under way

their second Pye platter, 'Warpaint', cracked the UK Top 20, and they also cleaned up with 'Ain't Gonna Wash For A Week' a few months later. Again, these were covers, the original American versions coming from Barry Mann and Eddie Hodges respectively. For a while the Brook Brothers were a hot property, and there was even talk of them starring in a Johnny Worth-penned West End musical, 'The James Boys', based on the exploits of the infamous Western badmen Frank and Jesse James. They toured with acts like Cliff Richard, Bobby Rydell and Jimmy Jones, appeared in the film *It's Trad, Dad!* and saw a few more singles slip into the lower reaches of the chart. Hatch, whose skills had helped made their singles stand out, deservedly went on to greater things, but the Brooks were soon passengers on the 'Oblivion Express'.

Radio Times

POP IN THE MEDIA

In America, disc jockeys such as Alan Freed and Dick Clark were regarded – quite rightly – as rock'n'roll heroes. Their musical taste influenced tens of thousands of teenagers and literally helped shape rock. They were mobbed wherever they went, their stage shows were sell-outs across the nation, and Freed even starred in a handful of films. However, the idea of a man who simply played records being an idol comparable to the record stars themselves seemed alien to most British teenagers in the mid-1950s.

When it is explained to Americans that Britain had no Top 40, R&B or country music radio stations, and that the nation never saw Dick Clark's *Bandstand* show, or other influential TV programmes like those of Ed Sullivan, Steve Allen (seen only in a couple of UK areas) and Milton Berle, many are amazed that rock'n'roll could ever have happened here at all.

Alan Freed, the legendary disc jockey credited more than anyone with the launch of rock'n'roll music

At that time, there was a vast difference in lifestyles between British and American youth. The average American teenager was thought to cruise around in a car (albeit dad's) with the radio blasting out raucous rock'n'roll music interrupted only by a manic sounding disc jockey, or a collection of cute commercials. The average British teenager, on the other hand, had no access to a car and, apart from listening to European radio stations, had only the staid and boring commercial-free BBC radioprogrammes to tune in to. This gave youngsters about a one in fifty chance of hearing a rock record, and no hope at all of hearing a presenter who sounded the slightest bit interested in their kind of music.

The most popular BBC station, the Light Programme, broadcast several shows featuring so-called 'popular' music, but in the late 1950s rock'n'roll fans found little of interest in their schedules. The music programmes with the most listeners on 'the Light' were *Housewive's Choice* and *Two Way Family Favourites* (a link-up with the British troops in Germany), both of which would play the occasional rock. Chances were that if you heard a rock song on another show it would be part of a live session by a second-rate UK act, or a band whose hey-day had been during the blitz. One of the main reasons for the lack of hits heard on air was the shortage of what was known as needle time (the Musicians Union insisted that live music took up a large proportion of the air time on BBC radio). Another was simply that the radio producers, and indeed most presenters, readily admitted they would rather be spinning platters by Frank Sinatra or Peggy Lee than rock. By the early 1960s, the BBC aired

Although radio and television were becoming increasingly influential, the records themselves remained the prime medium for pop music

(usually only at weekends and weekday lunch times) youth orient- ed programmes like *Saturday Club* (which started as *Saturday Skiffle Club*), *Pick Of The Pops*, Jack Jackson's *Record Roundabout*, *Go Man Go* which featured the Oscar Rabin band, *Ring A Ding Ding*, Brian Matthews' *Easy Beat* (which replaced *Seventeen To 20 club*) and the lunch time shows, *Twelve O'clock Spin* and *Parade of The Pops*. These were an improvement, but 'needle time' still meant they were nothing like the US Top 40 shows; for that type of programme, teens had to tune to 'crack- ly' European stations like Luxembourg or Hilversum (in Holland).

Juke Box Jury with a typical line-up of hipsters featuring (left to right) radio presenter Sam Costa, actress June Marlow, DJ Jack Jackson and an actual pop star, Brenda Lee

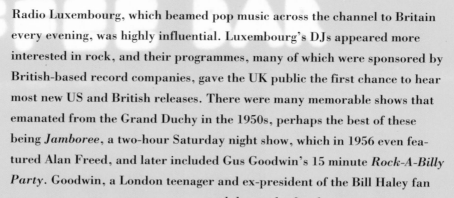

A *Boy Meets Girl* all-star cast, with (left to right) Billy Fury, Jess Conrad, Gene Vincent, Joe Brown, Eddie Cochran, Adam Faith and Marty Wilde

Radio Luxembourg, which beamed pop music across the channel to Britain every evening, was highly influential. Luxembourg's DJs appeared more interested in rock, and their programmes, many of which were sponsored by British-based record companies, gave the UK public the first chance to hear most new US and British releases. There were many memorable shows that emanated from the Grand Duchy in the 1950s, perhaps the best of these being *Jamboree*, a two-hour Saturday night show, which in 1956 even featured Alan Freed, and later included Gus Goodwin's 15 minute *Rock-A-Billy Party*. Goodwin, a London teenager and ex-president of the Bill Haley fan club, was by far the most exciting UK DJ, and became so popular that for a while he had four separate shows running on Luxembourg. He loved rock, and conveyed his excitement over the air waves, making his programme the high spot of many listeners' week. Among the many other noteworthy shows aired on Luxembourg in the early rock era were 'Top Twenty' (Britain's first radio chart show) on a Sunday night, Jimmy Saville's *Teen & Twenty Disc Club*, Jack Jackson's *D.E.C.C.A. Show* and various 15 minute programmes spotlighting Elvis, Cliff, Marty Wilde and Billy Fury. A survey in 1961 showed that the station (which existed from 1930 to 1992 and gave many Top UK DJs their start) had an average audience of over two million in the UK, more than the Home Service, the second most popular BBC station.

When rock arrived in the UK, television was the new young medium. However, this did not mean that it was any more open to rock'n'roll than radio. Unlike their American counterparts, British viewers could not see the likes of Elvis, Jerry Lee and Buddy Holly performing live on the small screen, since the *Perry Como Show* was the only nationally-aired US TV series. The only other hope of seeing a pop star on TV would be if they appeared on a British variety show, and you could bet your 78 collection that the vast majority of acts on such programmes would be home-grown, smile-as-you-sing graduates from the academy of all-round entertainment.

Understandably, the arrival of AR-TVs *Cool For Cats* on New Years Day 1957, and BBC's *6. 5 Special* a month later came as a great shock to the majority of the population, and as manna from heaven to a burgeoning army of rock-ravenous teenagers. *Cool For Cats* was a 15 minute programme that featured a dance troup performing well-choreographed routines to a handful of new releases. Hosted by Canadian Kent Walton, it ran for several years and was an important step forward, but due to its lack of live artists, did not have the same impact as *6.5 Special*. This low budget (£1,000 total per programme) show, which was the brainchild of TV producer Jack Good and presenter Josephine (later shortened to the teenager-friendly Jo) Douglas, at last gave viewers the opportunity to regularly see rock performed on the small screen. Welcome as *6.5 Special* was, it must be said that the programme is often viewed in retrospect as being more gutsy than it really was. It was in effect a musical show, aimed as much at fans of big bands, jazz and run-of-the-mill popular music as it was to followers of pure rock. At the time any programme with the occasional rock'n'roll act or record in it would have been as warmly welcomed as this musical hotch-potch. *6.5 Special* was presented by Pete Murray, one of those aforementioned radio DJs whose musical preference was for so called 'good music', and co-producer Douglas, a pleasant 'big sister' figure who would have been more at home as a children's TV presenter. They were often joined by ex-heavyweight boxer Freddie Mills – a forerunner of such latter-day talents as Henry Cooper and Frank Bruno – and the supposedly comical Mike & Bernie Winters, who only small children might have found slightly amusing.

Don Lang and his Frantic Five watched (to his left) by regular *6.5* presenters Pete Murray, Josephine Douglas and boxer Freddie Mills

An aerial view of the BBC studio during a *6.5 Special* live broadcast

Another 6.5 Special about to go on the air – and in those days it was completely live

The most regular riders on the *6-5 Special* were ex-jazz trombonist Don Lang and his Frantic Five (who were all well past their first flush of youth). In its two year run, every British rocker appeared on the show, as did many of the popular post-war big bands, droves of sequin-bedecked and dated divas and a collection of clean-cut balladeers from an earlier era. Arguably the high spots of the 55 minute show were the film clips (mostly from as yet unreleased movies) of such acts as Elvis, Little Richard and Jerry Lee Lewis, and the occasional 'record of the week' spot, which gave viewers a chance to hear a current US rock hit. Producer Good had a running battle with the BBC over the amount of rock'n'roll in the show. He had a great ear for rock and a good eye for new talent – Marty Wilde, Adam Faith, Terry Dene, Jim Dale and Jackie Dennis all got their first big breaks when they appeared on the programme.

6-5 Special was the most publicised and talked about British Television programme of its time - it opened TV's doors to rock, set up the goal posts which would be quickly widened by subsequent shows, and most importantly inspired scores of young Britons to become rock performers.

It was a genuinely live show and, sadly, none of the programmes were taped. Footage from the small-budget film of the same-name is all that remains of this pioneering show. *6-5 Special* finally ran out of steam at the end of 1958, having lost its way after Good left the BBC and moved over to the commercially based ATV to produce *Oh Boy!*.

Oh Boy!, the fastest paced and probably the best of Good's shows, ran from September 1958 to May 1959 and was aimed solidly at a teenage audience. During its run, all the top UK rockers appeared along with a handful of unconvincing ageing would-be teen idols. However, the fact that it was performed in front of a very live and responsive audience, who screamed continuously throughout, helped cover up any of these casting problems. Incidentally, on the first show Good launched a singer whose debut single he called 'the most amazing first record made by any UK teenager' and added 'make a note of the name Cliff Richard. You could be hearing quite a lot more of him.'

Demonstrations of how to jive expertly were a regular feature on youth-oriented pop TV programmes

Good's next venture into pop television, *Boy Meets Girls*, was screened from September 1959 to March 1960. Good now refers to the show as 'a dreadful mistake' but it did let the British public see live for the first time many top line US acts including Gene Vincent, Eddie Cochran, Conway Twitty, Johnny Cash, Freddy Cannon and Ronnie Hawkins. Two of the show's most popular artists, Marty Wilde and Billy Fury, went on to co-host Good's last regular UK TV series *Wham!* which ran for just nine weeks in 1960. Like his previous shows, it showcased the cream of Britain's rock and pop stars and gave invaluable exposure to many worthy new records and artists.

BBC TV tried not to let Good have it all his own way. *Dig This*, launched in January 1959, was a so-called, so-so pop music show which starred the middle-aged Bob Miller and his jazz-oriented band, and younger MOR vocalists like Barbara Young and Barry Barnett. It appeared that the show's producers were trying to tempt innocent young people away from the evils of rock to a type of music that their parents would approve of. The BBC followed this semi-disaster in April 1959, with *Drumbeat*, another mish-mash of musical styles that failed to work, and came off the air in August that year.

Most successful of the later BBC shows was undoubtedly *Juke Box Jury* which was launched in June 1959. It was the anglicised version of an American TV show, with smooth 'easy listening' DJ David Jacobs taking the role Peter Potter had filled Stateside. The plusses for the show were that one could hear a batch of new singles (often for the first time) but to do this you had to sit through a programme where the celebrity guests (usually from every field of entertainment excluding pop music) showed their complete ignorance of the current music scene, even making the show's genial, though out of touch, host seem knowledgeable.

In September 1961, the ABC-TV series *Thank Your Lucky Stars* was seen nationwide for the first time. The all-star programme soon became the pop show of the era and in the early

The Jack Good spotlight regularly fell on Saturday-night regulars like Marty (below, left) and Cliff (right)

The full *Oh Boy!* backing ensemble included (left to right) Neville Taylor's Cutters, the Vernons Girls, the Dallas Boys and Harry Robinson conducting Lord Rockingham's XI with Cherry Wainer on organ

years of the beat boom, all the UK's Top acts including The Beatles would fight it out to be on the show hosted by the amiable if patronising DJ, Brian Matthew.

Among the other TV shows in those early rock years, which might feature guests from the pop music world were: *Like…Music*, *Song Parade*, Jack Payne's shows *Off The Record*, *Words & Music* and *Say it With Music*, *Top Numbers*, *Crescendo*, and the Kent Walton hosted *Discs-A-Gogo*. There was also *The Big Show*, *The Jack Jackson Show*, the daily programme *Lunch Box*, *The Henry Hall Show*, *Swing Along* hosted by Marion Ryan, *Meet The Stars* and the 15 minute *Late Show*. Other shows that included pop personalities were *Trad Fad*, Granada TV's *Youngsters*, *Hits & Misses* with Dennis Lotis, *Joy Ride*, *Music Shop*, Westward TV's *Spin Along*, *Song Parade*, ATV's *Disc Break*, Alan Melville's *Parade* and *A-Z*, *Hits & Misses*, *Music With A Beat*, Granada's big band show *Bandstand*, *Top Tune Time* and *Be My Guest* hosted by Joan Regan. There were also the top rated TV variety programmes like *Sunday Night At The London Palladium*, *Saturday Spectacular*, *Saturday Show*, Val Parnell's *Startime*, *The Billy Cotton Band Show* and *The Morcambe & Wise Show*, *The Sunday Show*, AR-TV's *Hippodrome*, *Holiday Town Parade*, Jackie Rae's *The Variety Show*, *Chelsea At Nine*, *The Sunday Break* and a selection of shows head-lined by top comedians or MOR performers like Russ Conway and Dickie Valentine.

At a glance, there would seem to have been enough pop on TV in those days for everyone's taste, but it's easy to be misled. The shows, on average, would only include one pop artist a week and very rarely would that performer be rock-oriented; also many of these programmes only survived briefly, and several were only shown in one or two local regions.

The musical press were extremely important in this era. The *NME* was the most influential publication, and the biggest seller with a circulation of over 200,000 by 1962. Compared to its size today, it was extraordinarily small, boasting only 12 pages, crammed full of news and interviews with a mixture of top acts and new chart faces. *Record Mirror* and *Disc* (launched in February 1958) followed a similar format, whereas *Melody Maker*, the only other weekly pop music paper on sale, concentrated more on jazz. The *NME* was the first magazine to introduce a top selling records chart (a Top 12 in November 1952), and *Record Mirror* became the first to include a Top 50 chart (March 1962). All four magazines compiled their own charts, but it was the *NME* Top 30 that was treated as the official one (even after the music trade magazine *Record Retailer* launched their Top 50 in March 1960).

When payola and chart rigging in the early rock years are discussed, the British music industry usually comes out looking remarkably clean and honest compared to its American cousin. No doubt there is a lot of truth in that, although it may be worth noting that the editorial content of some magazines, quite coincidentally, often related to the advertisements taken, and that should anyone have wanted to falsify chart placings, it would have been a much simpler and cheaper process then than it would be today.

In January, 1959, Jack Good, the man behind the best of the early UK rock TV shows prophesied 'It will ultimately become standard practice for every artist to make a film of themselves performing their record. These short films will be sent to TV producers for their programmes.' He also foresaw 'It would not be a disc at all but a video tape - and you would play it on your television which would have a recorder-like attachment, which would also allow you to record your favourite TV programmes.' In the early 1960s, the first video juke boxes appeared courtesy of Cinebox in Italy and Scopitone in France. In Britain, Radiovision produced the UK's earliest music videos in 1962, and these colour films could be seen for one shilling (5p) on 19" screens above video juke boxes. The initial interest in these videos soon died down, and they were quickly forgotten along with Good's hare-brained predictions.

Studio dancers in a very early edition of the longest-running TV pop programme of all, the BBC's *Top of the Pops*

What Do You Want?

The Early Sixties

Much has been written about the reasons for the softening of rock'n'roll towards the tail end of the 1950s. Theories put forward include Elvis' recruitment into the army, the tragic death of Buddy Holly, Jerry Lee Lewis marrying a minor, Alan Freed's payola scandal, Chuck Berry's arrest (for taking an under-age girl across a state border) and Little Richard's exchange of rock for religion. All these factors may have contributed to the premature end of raw rock, but the fact is that the general record-buying public (steered cleverly towards their decision by the music industry) seemed to want to revert to more melodic songs and more refined and 'respectable' artists. Whatever the reason, this much-diluted version of mid-decade rock'n'roll was enthusiastically received on both sides of the Atlantic and, as rock gradually merged with pop, it often became impossible to say where one stopped and the other started. The average man in the street still did not consider pop/rock to be 'good' music, but felt it was becoming bearable.

The wild style of rock'n'roll pioneers like Jerry Lee Lewis (below) gradually gave way to politer pop as the late Fifties mellowed into the opening years of the Sixties

As the fabulous fifties drew to a close, many of the original first-generation rockers had already passed their artistic and commercial peaks, and their places in fans' hearts and in the charts, had been taken by a new breed of singer who refined rough-edged rock and made it more palatable to a wider audience. In Britain rock's second generation was generally less reliant on covering American songs and spent less time looking across the Atlantic for ideas and inspiration. There is no denying that the majority of songs that became hits in Britain still flowed from the pens of North American composers, but a healthy and increasing percentage were home- grown and more and more of these were being written by the actual artists who performed them.

By 1959 the music business in Britain had resigned itself to the fact that rock sold records, and almost every label's artist roster included at least a handful of rock-related acts, of which only a small percentage could become stars. Parlophone Records A&R head George Martin said, 'It's hard to find a rock singer who can break through, as there are so many of them'. He added, 'I intend to persevere in my search since it's obvious that the rock influence is here for all time.' When asked what he looked for in a new rock act, Martin said, 'a distinctive sound which, at the same time, is attractive.'

One of the most distinctive new singers of the period was Anthony Newley, whose role in the 1959 film *Idle On*

Parade turned the 28-year-old actor, with the unmistakable quavering voice into a hit parade idol. Newley, whose previous main claim to fame had been playing the Artful Dodger in David Lean's 1949 film of *Oliver Twist*, climbed into the Top 3 with the Jerry Lordan ballad 'I've Waited So Long', and an EP of songs from the film (which included this hit, and two songs Newley had co-written) also reached the Top 20. The success came as a big surprise to Newley, who admitted, 'This was the first time anyone had let me sing in a film, and I only recorded the songs for a giggle.' He added, 'Nobody connected with the film expected they would be hits, as the film knocks the rock, it is a satire of rock'n'roll. Across the Atlantic, it was a different story – a reviewer condemned the film as 'an awful attempt to pass Newley off as a rock star', adding, 'the songs are terrible.' Despite his unexpected British success Newley was adamant about his future career: 'Acting is what I have been trained to do and is my chosen profession. One hit does not mean that I am now a singer.' However, record buyers disagreed, and his follow-up, the contagious Lloyd Price song, 'Personality', pipped Price's platter at the post in the UK, becoming the second of 10 Top 20 singles that he would accumulate before successfully turning his attention to Broadway and Hollywood.

Another veteran performer who suddenly found himself in the limelight in 1959 was Bert Weedon, a guitarist who had conceivably played on more hit records than any other axe man of his era. Weedon, whose guitar instruction book was an invaluable tool to many of Britain's later guitar heroes, was a classically trained musician who candidly admitted, 'Playing rock is sometimes a bring down, especially after practising so hard to achieve a good pure tone. However, I'll always go along with the trend, and if the public wants a clangy guitar sound, I'll oblige!' In 1959, his clangy revival of Arthur Smith's 1948 instrumental 'Guitar Boogie Shuffle' (which was a cover of an American hit by The Virtues) gave this unlikely Hit Parade hero his only Top 10 single.

Standing alongside Weedon in the Top 20 was the debut hit by a singer less than half his age, Craig Douglas, who was to become the most successful of a brigade of 'boy-next-door' pop performers who appeared on the UK scene as the 1950s drew to an end. The 18-year-old ex-milkman had a couple of unrewarding releases on Decca before following his producer Dick Rowe to the Top Rank label in 1959. His first chart success came with the memorable 'A Teenager In Love', a Doc Pomus & Mort Shuman song popularised in the US by Dion & The Belmonts. By the end of the year Douglas had

Long after his chart successes of the early Sixties, Craig Douglas' record releases included a vocal version of the theme from the TV series *Tales Of The Unexpected*

Antony Newley's career has summed up the ambition of many a Fifties pop singer: to write a Broadway musical, to be an 'all-round entertainer', and to marry Joan Collins!

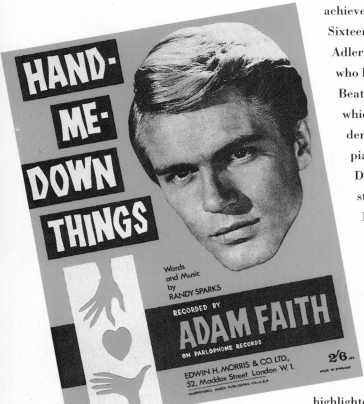

HAND-
ME-
DOWN
THINGS

Words
and Music
by
RANDY SPARKS

RECORDED BY

ADAM FAITH

ON PARLOPHONE RECORDS

EDWIN H. MORRIS & CO. LTD.,
52, Maddox Street London W. 1.

2/6 NET

MADE IN ENGLAND

CHERRYBELL MUSIC PUBLISHING CO., U.S.A

Adam Faith's good looks and for-the-time trendy
image made him one of the true pin-ups of the early
Sixties pop scene

Adam Faith's backing group
The Roulettes included guitarist
Russ Ballard, who was later part of
Unit 4+2 and the early-Seventies
hitmakers Argent

achieved the biggest hit of his career with another tale of teen love, 'Only Sixteen', a song first recorded by Sam Cooke and penned by Cooke, Lou Adler (later boss of Dunhill Records) and Herb Alpert, a musical alchemist who later discovered the secret of turning brass into gold. Before The Beatles arrived, Douglas had amassed nine UK Top 20 singles, only one of which featured an original song. The hit in question was yet another tender teen tune, 'The Heart Of A Teenage Girl', co-written by eccentric pianist Morgan 'Thunderclap' Jones. The amiable and well-scrubbed Douglas, who was on a par with Pat Boone in the rough'n'rowdy stakes, was Britain's premier 'parent-preferred' teen idol in the early 1960s.

In an inevitably unsuccessful attempt to break into the US chart, Douglas recorded a version of 'What Do You Want', the song that had shot the gaunt Adam Faith to the top of the UK chart. Faith, like Douglas, was not an overnight sensation, having had three unrewarding single releases before scoring the first of his seven successive Top 5 hits. He performed the undeniably catchy 'What Do You Want' using the vocal inflections of Buddy Holly highlighted in an exaggerated version of the late star's pronunciation of baby ('bay-bee'), while a nine-piece string section played a scintillating pizzicato arrangement (similar to that on Holly's 'It Doesn't Matter Anymore' - a song Faith later recorded himself) behind him. When asked about his mannered diction, Faith replied 'The bay-bee business wasn't pre-planned - it just seemed to develop in the studio. When you make a record these days you've got to pull something out of the bag.' The follow-up, 'Poor Me (also the title of his later autobiography), which trod familiar turf, also reached No.1, and during the early 1960s, only Cliff Richard was more popular with teenagers in Britain. Unlike those of most of his contemporaries, the vast majority of Faith's hits were British songs, which, for a change, meant that American acts covered his records. Surprisingly, however, none of his hit songs charted Stateside, even though they were cut by top acts like Bobby Vee ('What Do You Want') and Fabian ('Made You'). It was rare in those days for a pop singer to appear on TV chat shows, but Faith was an exception, and his coherent – indeed articulate – conversation helped redefine the way many of the older generation viewed rock stars.

The last month of the 1950s found another new name at the top of the UK charts, Emile Ford & The Checkmates. Ford, who hailed from the West Indies, was the first

British-based black vocalist to reach No. 1 (pianist Winifred Atwell had twice made the journey to the summit in the mid-1950s), and was one of the first artists to sell over a million copies of a single in the UK alone. Ford and his multi-racial group The Checkmates debuted with 'What Do You Want To Make Those Eyes At Me For' (the song returned to the Top 5 in 1987 in a version by Shakin' Stevens), which replaced 'What Do You Want' at the top and headed the charts for five weeks (trivia buffs might like to note that this was the only time that the title of a No. 1 was completely included in the title of the record that replaced it). The combo became a regular fixture in the Top 30 over the next 18 months and were voted Best New Act of 1960 by the *NME* readers. Incidentally, their supporting acts on the road in 1962 included an up-and-coming group from Liverpool, The Beatles.

Amongst other artists who made their chart debuts in 1959 were beat ballad merchants Mike Preston and David McBeth, who both spent a sojourn in the spotlight thanks to their versions of The Fleetwoods' haunting American chart topper 'Mr. Blue'. They were to be the last of a long line of MOR-based singers to make their mark during this decade, and might have been chart regulars if they had appeared on the scene five years earlier, when their vocal style and image were more in vogue.

Just for the record, among the new British male singers who recorded with minimal success in the late 1950s were *Drumbeat* regular Barry Barnett, Barry Cryer (now a well-known TV personality and comedy writer) and Gerry Dorsey (who later re-emerged as Engelbert Humperdinck). There were also Larry Parnes' protégés Johnny Gentle and the highly regarded Duffy Power, Eddie Hickey, West Indian beat balladeer Jimmy Lloyd, Mal Perry, producer Joe Meeks' discovery Danny Rives, Russ Sainty (who is now in the Dallas Boys), Al Saxon, who charted with a cover of 'Only Sixteen', and Dean Webb.

The route that most British artists were obliged to follow to reach the charts in the first year of the 1960s was, not surprisingly, very similar to the path followed by their predecessors at the end of the previous decade. The 2 I's coffee-bar continued for another year or so as the place for new talent to emerge, Larry Parnes was still the quintessential manager, Jack Good remained the TV producer to impress, no notable new labels had leapt into the limelight, and musically the late Buddy Holly was still a major influence.

US idol Fabian was actually launched on the basis that he looked like a cross between Elvis Presley and Ricky Nelson!

Although not a big record seller in the UK, Fabian and others like him were typical of the 'formula faces' that graced the covers of pop magazines on both sides of the Atlantic

117

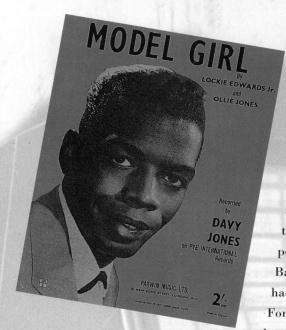

Davy Jones (above) was one of the few black singers on the British pop scene at the time

Ricky Valance (below) scored with 'Laura' but failed to follow it up

The first successful new face in the swinging Sixties was Lance Fortune who, after being spotted singing at the 2 I's by Larry Parnes, had been added to Gene Vincent's first UK tour. His debut disc 'Be Mine', which closely resembled recordings by the Holly-influenced Adam Faith, was a slow starter but eventually climbed into the Top 10, thanks in no small part to the string arrangement from Faith's musical director John Barry (under the name Johnny Prendy - his real name being John Barry Prendergast). Fame for Fortune was fleeting, and as his sole hit slipped down the chart, Barry himself jumped into the Top 20 for the first time with 'Hit And Miss', a lively instrumental that he had composed as the theme to the top-rated pop TV show, *Juke Box Jury*. This John Barry Seven single naturally also featured that pizzicato string sound that had been popularised via Barry's distinctive arrangements for Faith and Fortune. Barry was no newcomer to the UK pop business; he had been a regular on *6.5 Special*, *Oh Boy!* and *Drumbeat*, and had recorded several stiffs before hitting on a winning formula. He said, 'In the early days I used to copy the Americans, but it didn't get me anywhere. When I failed at that the only alternative was to try something original.' A couple of months later Barry's group were voted second Small British Group (to The Shadows) in the *NME* poll, and in 1961 had their only Top 10 hit, a timely cover of The Ventures' first American Top 10 entry, '*Walk Don't Run*'. In late 1961 Barry had a call from Hollywood, and the rest, as they so often say, is history.

Back in 1956, when the John Barry Seven were often likened to American rock band Freddie Bell & The Bellboys, their line-up included singer/guitarist Keith Kelly, an old RAF friend of Barry. After leaving the group in 1959 Kelly was spotted performing at the 2 I's by George Martin, who signed him to Parlophone. Martin thought this young man, whose glasses gave him a distinct Buddy Holly look, might be the rock singer/songwriting act that he had been looking for. Initially, Martin's faith seemed justified when Kelly had a double-sided hit in 1960 with his maiden release, 'Tease Me' and 'Ooh-La-La'. However, none of his later singles lived up to his earlier promise and Kelly, who had penned his hooky hit on a London underground train, soon found that his solo career had gone down the tube.

At the same time that Martin was having problems returning Kelly to the chart, Jerry Lordan, another singer/songwriter on Parlophone, was also having difficulty renewing his passport to the Hit Parade. Lordan, who had written the Top 3 hit 'I've Waited So Long' for Anthony Newley, was having trouble following his first two Top 30 hits as a singer, 'I'll Stay Single' and 'Who Could Be Bluer'. The songwriter-turned-singer could not fathom out why fans had bought his first releases and ignored his later ones. However, he soon resigned himself to the fact that he should concentrate on songwriting, saying, ' I like singing, but I like writing even more…firstly because I do it better and secondly because it's more rewarding.' Lordan, who incidentally could not read or write music, became one of the most successful British songwriters of the early 1960s, while George Martin continued his hunt for a rock act that could write their own hit material.

While Kelly and Lordan were bemoaning the fact that they were having trouble returning to the Top 20, there were many talented new male singers that year who would have gladly changed places with them. You can count among the number Johnny Carson, Jimmy Crawford (who reached the Top 30 with a version of The Paris Sisters' 'I Love How You Love Me'), Bobby Deacon, Eddie Falcon, Perry Ford and Jody Gibson. Other worthy artists include Terence Holderway Hale, Paul Hanford, Danny Hunter, Nelson Keene (who almost cracked it with a cover of 'Image Of A Girl'), Steve Perry, Paul Raven (who became a 1970s superstar when he changed his name to Gary Glitter), Mike Sagar, Dave Sampson (who came close with a cover of 'Sweet Dreams'), Dean Shannon, Chris Wayne and Joe Meek's West Indian protégé Ricky Wayne (a future 'Mr. World').

Jack Good still set the standards for pop TV in 1960. His series *Boy Meets Girls* (which followed *Oh Boy!*) ended its six month run in March, and it was soon followed by *Wham!*, a short-lived series hosted by Marty Wilde and Billy Fury. One of the lesser-known artists who appeared on all three programmes was Michael Cox, a lanky lad from Liverpool, whose career reached its peak in the summer of 1960, when his Joe Meek-produced version of Johnny Ferguson's US Top 40 hit 'Angela Jones' bounded up the Best Sellers. The ultra-commercial song was to be both Cox's and Ferguson's entry ticket to one-hit wonderland. Two other British singers also bound for that destination in 1960 were Garry Mills and Ricky Valance. Mills, who was probably the last hit-maker to be spotted at the 2 I's coffee-bar, had his sole Top 20 entry with the film theme 'Look For A Star'. Until that record he had regularly, albeit unsuccessfully, covered American hits, and it's ironic that US covers of his British Top 5 entry, almost certainly stopped it repeating its success Stateside.

Neville Taylor with his Cutters was a regular part of the '*Oh Boy!*' television line-up, but unfortunately failed to cut it in the record charts

FIRST WORDS OF LOVE

By SEAN O'MAHONY

2/-

Featured & Recorded by
NEVILLE TAYLOR

Columbia Records artist Valance was helped to the top of the chart by rival label Decca, who refused to release Ray Peterson's original version of the controversial death disc, 'Tell Laura I Love Her'. By the time Decca decided to issue their superior recording, Valance was already motoring up the chart at full throttle, leaving the other UK cover version by John Leyton many laps behind.

John Leyton was an actor and would-be singer whose regular appearances in the TV series *Biggles* had inspired Joe Meek to sign him in 1960 (he had failed auditions with Pye and EMI). In July 1961, after a couple of poor-selling singles, he appeared as rock singer Johnny St. Cyr (sincere!) in the ATV series, *Harper's West One*, and the role gave him the opportunity to sing (a couple of times) his third release, 'Johnny Remember Me'. Incidentally, at the eleventh hour part of the lyric of this Geoff Goddard-composed death song was revised from 'the girl I loved who died a year ago' to 'the girl I loved and lost a year ago'. The response was instant, and by its release date the haunting song had built up advance orders of almost 40,000 copies. A month later it was topping the chart, and over the next nine months Leyton put a further three singles into the Top 20. He soon became one of the most popular pin-ups of the period, and was voted the Top New Singer of the Year. However, the actor/singer, whose looks had helped take him to the top, found that when the beat groups arrived his face no longer fitted.

Riding the beat bandwaggon, Eden Kane with his backing group The Downbeats

Eden Kane's brother Peter Sarstedt was another chart-topper with the 1969 smash 'Where Do You Go To My Lovely'

This was not the first time that playing a rock'n'roll singer had resulted in the actor becoming a rock star. In America in 1957 Tommy Sands (who was an unsuccessful C&W artist) had played a rocker in the TV play, *The Singing Idol*, and overnight had become a rock idol himself. Actor Ricky Nelson also discovered that performing rock'n'roll on TV (he starred in his parent's situation comedy *The Adventures of Ozzie & Harriet*) did nothing but good for his singing career. Probably the earliest British TV play about a rock star was *Rock-A-Bye Barney* in 1959, starring Jess Conrad, who in the play mimed to the voice of Garry Mills. Conrad's name often crops up when people discuss British singers of the early rock years, and his limitations as a singer have made him a legend. His recordings like 'This Pullover' have become collectors' items, thanks to their regularly making the 'World's Worst Records' lists. However, to be fair to Conrad, he was first and foremost an actor, and one of Britain's most successful young thespians in the early 1960s. To Conrad, singing was a secondary profession, and it should be noted that few, if any, critics at the time commented adversely on his vocal talent. In fact, the *NME*, who described his voice as 'friendly and appealing', selected Conrad as their 'Tip For Stardom' in 1961. He might have had difficulty hitting every note he aimed at (Dickie Pride sometimes helped out vocally in the studio), but he was not the only singer, then or now, whose personality and profile helped compensate for their vocal shortcomings.

Apart from John Leyton, the most successful new British vocalists in 1961 were Karl Denver and Eden Kane who, like Leyton, debuted on the chart as the summer drew to an end. The Karl Denver Trio were not a run-of-the-mill early 1960s pop act. Denver, who loved to sing folk and country songs taken from the four corners of the globe, had an ear-drum piercing, multi-octave vocal range, and a very commercial recording manager in Jack Good. His first single, a yodelling revival of the pre-World War I song 'Marcheta', introduced him to the Hit Parade and for the next two years Denver stockpiled single smashes. His biggest hit came with his stunning vocal interpretation of the African traditional song 'Wimoweh'. Although it was released when The Tokens US chart topping arrangement of the same song (which they retitled 'The Lion Sleeps Tonight') was in the UK Top 20, it quickly roared past it into the Top 3. Karl Denver added much-needed colour and contrast to the British record scene in 1961-2, as *NME*'s Derek Johnson noted: 'At a time when there have been a spate of unimaginative performers and carbon-copy artists, it is refreshing to find an artist with a totally different and distinctive approach.'

Eden Kane, who combined the looks and animal magnetism of an Elvis or Cliff with the sartorial elegance of Adam Faith, was the last major British teen idol before the arrival of The Beatles. He was a pop/beat singer who incorporated a distinctive growl into many of his records, perhaps to let listeners know that just below his polished surface there was a rough, raw rock'n'roller trying to break out. His second single, 'Well I Ask You', topped the UK chart, and was covered by a handful of acts in the US including Bobby Vinton and Kay Starr (although none made the Top 100), and was also given a 1920s treatment in Britain by Fred Walkingstick (!). Kane was a worrier, and after this first hit said, 'I realise that unless my future is planned carefully and I concentrate everything upon my career, I could disappear as other promising singers like Tommy Bruce, Ricky Valance and Garry Mills have.' As it transpired, Kane held on to his teen idol status for a relatively long time, scoring four Top 10 hits before the group explosion burst his bubble. On the premise that 'if you can't beat beat groups, then join them', he

Michael Cox released two different singles called 'Teenage Love', one in 1959 on Decca and one in 1961 on HMV

Another healthy-looking boy-next-door, Mark Wynter had a surprisingly long run of Top 30 hits in the early Sixties including the archetypal teen ballad 'Venus In Blue Jeans'

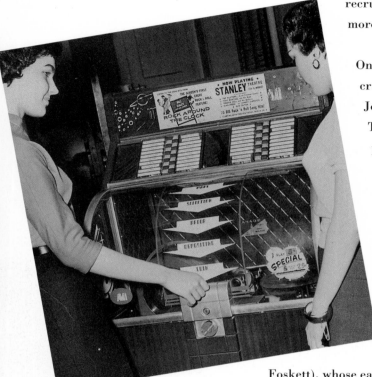

Juke Box Saturday Night: right up to the boom in live groups that exploded across the country in 1963, the juke box remained the focus of much social activity

Trevor Peacock, composer of Jess Conrad's 'Mystery Girl' also penned Herman's Hermits' 1965 hit 'Mrs.Brown You've Got A Lovely Daughter'

recruited The Downbeats and, with them behind him, managed one more Top 10 hit in 1964.

On September 9, 1961, the week that his second single 'Get Lost' crashed into the Top 20, Eden Kane growled his way through the Johnny Worth composition on the first nationwide showing of ABC-TV's *Thank Your Lucky Stars*. The show soon became the most popular pop music programme on British television, a position it held throughout the formative days of the beat boom that was to follow. The show helped launch the careers of many stars and one-hit wonders, including Doug Sheldon, Ricky Stevens (who made his TV debut on the show) and Shane Fenton & The Fentones. Fair-haired actor/singer Sheldon, who looked every inch a pop idol, was never really taken to the public's heart, spending about as long in the Top 20 with his sole hit, a cover of 'Runaround Sue', as the pioneer Russian cosmonaut Yuri Gagarin had recently spent in space. Diminutive London-born singer and saxophonist Ricky Stevens (real name Kenneth Foskett), whose early musical experience included playing in his family's band (he has nine brothers and four sisters!), was discovered singing in an East End pub by EMI's Norman Newell. Stevens inscribed his name in the Top 20 ledger with a unique falsetto yodelling version of the 1923 song 'I Cried For You (which Judy Garland had sung in the film *Babes In Arms*). It was to be the only chart entry for the man who had been given his stage name by his musical director Geoff Love. Unfortunately, an equally original interpretation of 'My Mother's Eyes' in 1963, didn't quite cancel his membership to the 'one-hit wonder club'.

Another act that found itself in that exclusive club was Shane Fenton & The Fentones, who snappy dresser Eden Kane described as 'The best-dressed, best-presented group around.' Their 1961 debut single 'I'm A Moody Guy', which had been especially written for them by Parlophone label-mate Jerry Lordan, ideally suited Fenton, whose image owed as much to early Elvis and Gene Vincent as to any later idols. The record paid a fleeting visit to Top 20, a feat the group were unable to repeat, although their cover of American actor Johnny Crawford's US hit, 'Cindy's Birthday' in 1962, almost gave them a happy return. By the time groups became the 'in' thing in 1963, Fenton and his Fentones looked and sounded decidedly dated, so there was to be no place for them in the swinging sixties. However, Fenton, unlike the vast majority of his contemporaries, was dusted off in the following decade and found stardom as Alvin Stardust.

1962 not only found *Thank Your Lucky Stars* going from strength to strength, but for the second year running it found TV producer Jack Good without a pop TV series. However, that did not mean that his influence was not still being felt. One of the year's most successful Top 20 debutantes was Joe Brown & The Bruvvers (cockney pronunciation of 'brothers') who had been one of Good's discoveries in the late 1950s. Brown, who started with the Spacemen skiffle group, was that rare commodity in the early days of rock, a UK vocalist who sang with a 100 per cent English accent. Like the earlier blonde-haired Cockney rocker, Tommy Steele, Brown had the kind of 'cheeky' personality that could have made him a major star in the music hall era. Again like Steele, Brown was signed to Larry Parnes, and pop mythology has it that Parnes tried to rechristen him Elmer Twitch! Thanks to his frequent appearances on Good's *Boy Meets Girls* in 1959, he became one of the most popular and easily recognisable UK rock stars, and his rousing revival of 'Darktown Strutters Ball' cracked the Top 30 in 1960. Despite releasing a handful of first rate records, Brown had to wait until mid-1962 for his first major hit, 'A Picture Of You', which went all the way to the top. The single, which incidentally was the 100th Silver Disc (for 250,000 sales) awarded in the UK, was composed by Bruvvers bassist Peter Oakman and was covered unsuccessfully in the US by such chart-worthy artists as Paul Evans and The Kalin Twins. Brown was voted UK Music Personality of the Year in 1962 and, thanks to two more Top 10 singles in 1963, he regained that title in the first year of Britain's beat boom. Perhaps if this one-time winkle salesman had arrived on the scene a couple of years later, his 'cute' regional accent, likable personality, sense of humour and high-quality songs, could have also made him a major star on the other side of the Atlantic.

Another solo performer who added a little fun to pop before the start of the group invasion was Mike Sarne, whose novelty Cockney beat duet with Wendy Richard, 'Come Outside', was the first record by a male/female duo to top the chart. Although his soundalike follow-up, 'Will I What' (on which Billie Davis played his foil), had reputed advance orders of over 100,000, it managed only a lowly Top 20 placing. It was to be the last major chart success for the London University student, who like his good friend John Leyton was managed by Robert Stigwood, while the talented young Charles Blackwell (who also wrote his chart topper) was his musical arranger.

The only British rock acts to top the UK album chart before the Beatles were The Shadows and their boss Cliff Richard

A more accomplished musician than his happy-go-lucky image suggested, Joe Brown is now recognised as a fine guitar player in the country-rock field

Like all years, 1961 and 1962 also had their chart casualties, acts who for one reason or another remained Top 20 virgins. Trivia freaks might like to add these names to the Honour Roll of Near Miss Artists: ex-Avon Ray Adams, Joe Meek protégé Andy Cavell, Don Charles and Neil Christian, Lee Corvette, Roly 'Yo-Yo' Daniels and Johnny De Little. Other singers who can be added to this if-only-they-had-got-the-breaks list are Frank Kelly, Brad Newman, Dean Rogers, successful songwriter Trevor Peacock, Rikki Price, Bobby Shafto and the very talented Mike Berry (whose biggest hits were ahead of him) and singer/songwriter Geoff Goddard.

By 1962 most British hit makers were not merely recording original material (which in itself was a laudable and long-awaited event): the songs, and in many cases the recordings and artists, were on a par with anything America had to offer. It was perhaps surprising, then, that the biggest-selling British recording on both sides of the Atlantic that year was Frank Ifield's revival of an old American song, 'I Remember You'. Ifield (who had intended to record the song since he first heard Kay Starr's version in 1958) said that at first producer Norrie Paramor was not keen on his version of the song. 'You've changed that song beyond recognition', Paramor told Ifield, 'you've changed the chords and added that falsetto bit, and I don't want to put my name to it as an arranger.' Paramor relented, however, and even added the catchy 'Waltzing Matilda' harmonica phrase. The record, which sold over a million in the UK alone and was voted Record of the Year in the *NME* poll, found itself nestling in the US Top 10 in the week that The Beatles debuted in the UK Top 30. In Britain this unmistakable singer and yodeller became the first artist to amass three successive Number Ones (which, incidentally, were all revivals of American songs), and in 1963 Frank Ifield was as popular in Britain as The Beatles.

Mike Berry (left) with fellow chart stars Susan Maughan and Ronnie Carroll. Susan is well-remembered for the bouncy 'Bobby's Girl', although she didn't make the same impact with a follow-up weepie 'Hand A Handkerchief To Helen'

One of Ifield's earliest supporters was Cliff Richard, who predicted (before the success of 'I Remember You'), 'I am sure it won't be long before Frank Ifield can count a whole string of hits to his credit.' Cliff also knew that his bass player, Jet Harris, would make it as a solo artist, and sure enough, within a month of leaving The Shadows in 1962, Harris' original treatment of Jimmy Dorsey's 1944 US No. 1, 'Besame Mucho', had flown into the top 30. His second single, an equally powerful version of Billy May's 1956 Top 10 hit, 'Main Title Theme From Man With The Golden Arm', then climbed into The Top 20. Harris was not a confident singer, but was persuaded by Jack Good to include some vocals in his recording repertoire and stage show. His first tour in late 1962 (on which he was backed by The Jetblacks) found him on the same bill as The Beatles, with both acts supporting Little Richard. When asked about the difference between his guitar sound and that of American star Duane Eddy, Harris commented 'mine is deeper, it's about six tones deeper.' Harris then teamed with another ex-Shadow, Tony Meehan, and their first record together, the Jerry Lordan composition, 'Diamonds' topped the chart for a month before being replaced by The Beatles' first No. 1 in the *NME* chart 'Please Please Me'.

The dynamic instrumental duo of Jet Harris (left) and Tony Meehan, who had three consecutive Top 5 entries in 1963

No chapter on early 1960s hit makers would be complete without returning to the subject of Cliff Richard who, between 1960 and The Beatles' first hit in late 1962, clocked up another dozen Top 5 entries. These ranged from first-class ballads like 'When The Girl In Your Arms' (covered in the US by Connie Francis) and 'I'm Looking Out The Window' (which Peggy Lee had previously recorded) to high-class out-and-out rockers like the Otis Blackwell song, 'Nine Times Out Of Ten', and Jerry Lee Lewis' 'It'll Be Me'. Cliff, of course, wasn't the only 1950s star to add to their catalogue of hits in the early 1960s. Lonnie Donegan, Billy Fury, Frankie Vaughan and Marty Wilde also regularly renewed their season ticket to the chart, but Cliff Richard was the only one to keep charting throughout the 1960s – not to mention the following three decades.

ANTHONY NEWLEY

A London born actor/singer/songwriter/cabaret performer/producer and director, who, as a teenager, played lead roles in the films *Vice Versa* (which also starred Petula Clark) and *Oliver Twist*, Newley had over 20 film parts under his belt before his role as the conscripted rock'n'roll singer Jeep Jackson in the 1959 film *Idle On*

TOP SINGLES 1962

1	**SHADOWS** **Wonderful Land** Columbia
2	**FRANK IFIELD** **I Remember You** Columbia
3	**TORNADOS** **Telstar** Decca
4	**CLIFF RICHARD** **The Young Ones** Columbia
5	**FRANK IFIELD** **Lovesick Blues** Columbia

Parade launched his musical career. Newley soon phased rock out of his repertoire, and by cleverly mixing original songs, well-chosen covers and unique arrangements of old favourites ensured himself regular chart visits over the next three years. He had two successive UK chart toppers in 1960, the gently sentimental ballad 'Why' and 'Do You Mind', a catchy Lionel Bart song, on which Newley was backed by only a rhythm section and Bart clicking his fingers. Of the former recording, Newley noted, 'We worked very hard to make me sound as innocuous as the original US version by Frankie Avalon, and I think we succeeded.' Newley has never been afraid of attempting the unusual; his quirky 1960 TV series, *The Strange World of Gurney Slade*, was a forerunner of many later shows, as was his very successful and equally off-beat 1961 stage musical *Stop the World - I Want To Get Off* (whose original cast album reached the Top 10), while who but Newley could have turned old chestnuts like 'Strawberry Fair' and the nursery rhyme 'Pop Goes The Weasel' into big hits? Subsequently celebrated because his mannered theatrical cockney phrasing was later aped by David Bowie, Newley wrote the oft-recorded ballads, 'Who Can I Turn To?' and 'What Kind of Fool Am I', the theme to the James Bond movie *Goldfinger*, and 'The Candy Man', a US No. 1 for his No. 1 fan, Sammy Davis. A multi-talented performer, he was married to Joan Collins, and has since starred on Broadway, headlined at Las Vegas and been involved with countless films and stage shows on both sides of the Atlantic.

Bring back the Bert! Thousands of guitar strummers remember with affection the first helping hand given by Bert Weedon as they fumbled their way around the chord changes

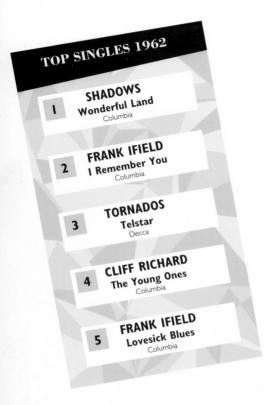

BERT WEEDON

This London-born guitarist, is perhaps best known as the author of the *Play In A Day* guitar manual, which has sold over a million copies. He played in his first band in 1937 and was a winner on the famous Caroll Levis Talent Show in 1939. After the war Weedon played with such notable musicians as Stephane Grappelli, Django Reinhardt, Ambrose and Ted Heath, before becoming the resident guitarist in Cyril Stapleton's noted Showband. In 1954 *NME* readers voted him Britain's No.1 guitarist, and in 1956 he released his debut single, 'Stranger Than Fiction', on Parlophone. He soon became a much sought after session player recording with top British MOR acts like Alma Cogan, Eddie Calvert and David Whitfield, and when rock arrived he was the most in-demand session guitarist in the UK, and could be heard on records by Tommy Steele, Terry Dene, Cliff Richard, Marty Wilde and Adam Faith as well as on more MOR-inclined recordings of the late 1950s by acts like Russ Conway and Laurie London. His only major solo success came with his treatment of The Virtues' US hit, 'Guitar Boogie Shuffle', although both 'Nashville Boogie' in 1959 and 'Sorry Robbie' in 1960 also reached the Top 30, and his original recording of 'Apache' (a No. 1 for The Shadows) only narrowly missed the chart. Despite the lack of hits, Weedon kept a high profile throughout the 1960s and in the 1970s, with his budget albums selling in large quantities, and the TV-advertised 22 Golden Guitar Greats even topping the album chart – nearly 40 years after his first gigs!

CRAIG DOUGLAS

Light beat and ballad singer Craig Douglas was born Terence Perkins on the Isle of Wight. At the age of 17 he was taken under the wing of successful manager/ agent/songwriter Bunny Lewis, who soon lined up a string of TV appearances for the clean-cut young performer. His first release in 1958 coupled covers of Marty Robbins' 'Sitting In A Treehouse' and Eddie Fontaine's rocker 'Nothin' Shakin'. This single and the follow-up, his interpretation of Jimmie Rodgers' American Top 10 ballad 'Are You Really Mine?', went nowhere. He joined the fledgling Top Rank label in 1959 and his second release, 'A Teenager In Love', took him into the Top 20. The follow-up, 'Only Sixteen', topped the chart (it was also Top Rank's first No. 1) and Douglas was voted the Top New Singer of 1959 in the *NME* poll. This British teen idol later reached the Top 10 with 'Pretty Blue Eyes', 'A Hundred Pounds Of Clay' (a semi-religious song that ran into trouble with the BBC), ' Time' and 'Our Favourite Melodies' (which included the refrains from a few recent hits), his versions helping to keep the original recordings respectively by Steve Lawrence, Gene McDaniels, Jerry Jackson and Gary Criss off the UK charts. When asked about the preponderance of cover versions in his recordings, Douglas admitted, 'one of my main worries is finding suitable new material', and added: 'The choice is usually left to Bunny Lewis, who has an incredible knack of picking winners, almost before they begin to move in the USA.' Douglas' wholesome, pleasant personality also made him palatable to an older audience and a natural for pantomime and films (he appeared in *Climb Up the Wall* and *It's Trad, Dad!*). The Beatles backed Douglas on their first major stage show, and it was arguably their arrival on the scene that helped cause the sudden erosion of his firm fan base.

The last of the saccharin smiles: Craig Douglas waves goodbye to the charts as the beat boys take over

ADAM FAITH

People started taking pop stars seriously for a change after Adam Faith appeared in an in-depth television interview discussing morality, God, the Universe, the meaning of life ....

Born Terry Nelhams in London, Adam Faith, like many of his predecessors, was discovered at the 2 I's cafe, where he was singing with the Worried Men skiffle group. Jack Good spotted his potential, and after a name change (Adam taken from a book of boys' names and Faith from a book of girls') booked him on *6.5 Special* in 1957. When his debut singles, 'Brother Heartache & Sister Tears' and a cover of Jerry Lee Lewis' wild rocker 'High School Confidential', failed to chart, HMV dropped his contract. Disillusioned with a solo career, he briefly sang in the duo Terry & Freddy (with ex-Viper Freddy Lloyd), before joining the regular team on BBC's pop TV show, *Drumbeat*. After his version of Thurston Harris' distinctive pop/R&B song, 'Ah! Poor Little Baby', on Top Rank Records (owned by the company for which he had worked as a messenger boy) failed to enter the charts, he signed with George Martin's Parlophone label. His first release, 'What Do You Want', rocketed him to super stardom, and gave the label its first chart topper. Faith, like America's new pin-up of the time Fabian (two of whose songs he recorded on his debut album), never claimed to possess a great voice - it was distinctive, but lightweight. However he knew his market, and his little-boy-lost songs hit the target with his predominantly female following, who wanted to mother the slightly built, well-dressed singer with the short-cropped blonde hair. Faith's face was soon seen in every teen magazine on the bookstands, and his live shows were greeted by pandemonium. He could also act and appeared in four films in 1960-2, confiding in 1960, 'I'm inclined to think that acting will be my real medium of acceptance.' Before that prophecy was fulfilled, he scored 14 successive Top 20 hits (nine of which made the Top 5), several of them after the arrival on the scene of his label-mates, The Beatles. During a lull in his career, Faith managed Leo Sayer and produced Sayer and Roger Daltrey. This astute artist, who appeared in several more movies, became a household name for the second time in the 1970s when he played the lead in the successful TV series *Budgie*. He celebrated five decades on the small screen by starring in the series *Love Hurts* in the early 1990s.

EMILE FORD & THE CHECKMATES

Emile Ford (real name Emile Sweatman) was born in the West Indies and lived in the Bahamas and St Lucia before moving to London in the mid-1950s to complete his studies. After some solo work in a London coffee bar, and a failed audition at Pye Records (in a calypso-styled duo with his brother), he formed The Checkmates in 1959. The group originally comprised brother George (bass), Ken Street (guitar), Alan Hawkshaw (keyboards) and John Cuffley (drums). They won the Soho talent competition, which led to a second, and this time successful, audition with Pye. Michael Barclay produced their first release on that label, the Don Gibson song, 'Don't Tell Me Your Troubles', but it was the B-side, a revival of a 1917 hit, 'What Do You Want To Make Those Eyes At Me For', which had been recorded in just half an hour, that topped the chart. Their treatment of the oldie was akin to the way US R&B act the Johnny Otis Show had recorded it a year earlier (Otis had thought his version would follow the lyrically similar, 'Ma, He's Making Eyes At Me', into the UK Top 10). Ford's radio-ripe recording, complete with false endings, went on to sell over a million copies in Britain alone. His follow-

The big voice of Emile Ford was ideally suited to the pub-song subtleties of his major hit 'What Do You Want To Make Those Eyes At Me For'

up, another oldie, 'On A Slow Boat To China', also sailed into the Top 5, and their next five singles, which included their Top 10 recording of Barry Mann's 'Counting Teardrops', reached the Top 30. Ford, whose favourite singer was Mario Lanza, said, 'Certainly I like rock'n'roll, and, in fact, I include it in my act. I like music with a beat and if it happens to be called rock'n'roll – which I know in some quarters is regarded as a dirty word – then it's just too bad.' Ford and the group (which had expanded to a seven piece and had added a female trio, The Fordettes) went their separate ways in 1963, and shortly afterwards he relocated to Sweden, returning later to play the UK club circuit. He was last reported to be running a successful electronics company.

British ballad singer Matt Monro was voted Top International Act and Most Promising Newcomer in the US *Billboard* 1961 DJ Poll

MIKE PRESTON

This ex-boxer and cartoon camera man was born Jack Davis and hailed from London. He was given his stage name in a competition by readers of Patrick Doncaster's pop music column in the *Daily Mirror*. A beat ballad singer, his first

release was the Jerry Lordan song 'A House, A Car and A Wedding Ring', recorded under the aegis of musical director Harry Robinson (the man behind the Lord Rockingham's XI sound). Although this Decca release sold only moderately well in the UK, it charted Stateside, and in 1958 Preston headed to the US where he appeared on the Alan Freed and Dick Clark shows. He continued to work as a cameraman until his commercial breakthrough in Britain came with the Joe Meek-produced 'Mr. Blue' in 1959. His second and last Top 20 hit came in 1961 with the ITV Song Contest winner 'Marry Me'. Anyone wishing to check out this rugged singer has only to watch the film *Climb Up the Wall* in which he appeared with Craig Douglas and Russ Conway.

DAVID MACBETH

MacBeth was a Newcastle-born light beat balladeer who was on the books of Newcastle United Football Club before being conscripted into the army. An appearance on the Caroll Levis Talent Show led to several local North Eastern Television spots (sometimes under the pseudonym of David North). In 1959, while he was working as a commercial traveller, Pye released his debut disc, 'Mr. Blue', a cover of the Fleetwood's US No. 1, which proved to be his only Top 20 success. He represented Britain at the European Knokke Festival in Belgium in 1962, and later that year his cover of Bobby Vinton's sing-along US chart topper 'Roses Are Red' managed to crack the Top 30. Though only a minor figure on the early 1960s British musical scene, MacBeth continued to work on the club circuit for many years, but his rare record releases failed to excite a public whose taste in singers had moved on.

JOHN LEYTON

This actor/singer from Essex (left), who was first seen in the TV series *The Invisible Man* in 1959, starred as Ginger in the successful Granada TV series *Biggles*. He was managed by Robert Stigwood (who later looked after acts like The Bee Gees and Eric Clapton) and signed by producer Joe Meek, whose unique sound helped make Leyton's records so distinctive and commercially successful. 'Johnny Remember Me', which he sang in the TV series *Harpers, West One*, was the first major hit for Leyton, Meek and its composer Geoff Goddard (whose first vocal number this was). When asked at the time about his thoughts on rock, Leyton commented, 'I think that basic rock is out. It has now advanced and developed and in its new form it's definitely here to stay. Melodies are coming back in a big way and now that rock and ballads are welding themselves together it seems to me that beat ballads are going to be the big thing for the next few months.' He was right, and in those next few months he put a further three beat ballads into the Top 20: 'Wild Wind' (which had over 300,000 advance orders), 'Son This Is She' and 'Lonely City' (all of these juke box favourites being produced by Meek and composed by Goddard). Leyton appeared in the 1962 film *It's Trad, Dad!* and in 1963, when his pop career was all but over, was one of the all-star cast in the celebrated war film, *The Great Escape*. In 1967 he played alongside Frank Sinatra in *Von Ryan's Express* and in 1985 his debut hit went back into the Top Three, courtesy of Bronski Beat & Marc Almond – who were among the many who remembered Johnny.

Jess Conrad came to epitomise, a trifle unfairly, the good-looking pop star with minimal vocal talent

JESS CONRAD

In 1959 the photogenic London born actor/singer and one time flower-seller Jess Conrad (real name Gerald James) played a r'n'r singer in both the ATV play *Rock-A-Bye Barney* and the Arthur Askey film *Friends and Neighbours*. As a singer he made his TV debut on St. Valentine's Day 1960 (exactly one year after *Rock-A-Bye Barney*) in *Boy Meets Girls*. Conrad, whose recording manager was Jack Good, and whose musical director was Charles Blackwell (who also worked with fellow actor/singer John Leyton), almost found instant success with his debut single 'Cherry Pie' (a cover of Skip & Flip's US hit). His only Top 20 entry came in 1961 with 'Mystery Girl', a song written for him by Trevor Peacock (about a girl Conrad saw every day passing his Dulwich home). Conrad, who is now the butt of many jokes, was voted the most popular artist on the *Wham!* TV series in 1961. He acted alongside Cliff Richard in the 1959 film *Serious Charge* and can also be seen in *The Ugly Duckling*, *Too Young To Marry*, *The Queen's Guard*, *Rag Doll*, *The Boys*, the horror film *Konga* and The Sex Pistols' 1979 mould-breaking rock movie *The Great Rock'n'Roll Swindle*.

LANCE FORTUNE

This pop/beat singer from Birkenhead, Cheshire (real name Chris Morris), studied classical piano until he received a guitar for Christmas in 1956. He sacrificed a scholarship to a Welsh university to work as an odd job man at London's famous

John Leyton (left) adopts a Sinatra-esque high-stool pose for that casual look favoured by balladeers on both sides of the Atlantic

British orchestra leader Mantovani received five gold albums on his arrival in the USA in 1961

coffee bar, the 2 I's, where he was spotted by impresario Larry Parnes. Parnes never actually managed him, but rechristened him Lance Fortune, a name he had previously given to singer/pianist Clive Powell, whom he later renamed Georgie Fame (get it - Fame and Fortune?). Fortune's fleeting five minutes of fame came courtesy of his first single, a Joe Meek-produced recording of the German song, 'Alle Mädchen Wollen Küssen' (which means 'All Girls Want Kisses'), for which tunesmith Marcel Stellman had written an English lyric entitled 'Be Mine'. The follow-up, 'This Love I Have For You', narrowly missed the Top 30, and Dame Fortune never again smiled on Lance.

Neither mean nor moody, Mike Sarne's innocuous pop song novelties were matched by an equally lightweight image

MIKE SARNE

Singer/actor Mike Sarne was born Michael Scheuer in London. Before recording, he had appeared (under the name Mike Shaw) in 10 films, including *The Guns of Navarone* and *Sink the Bismarck!* Sarne's debut disc, 'Come Outside', which also featured 18-year-old Yorkshire-born cockney (!) actress Wendy Richard, topped the chart in 1962. He followed it into the Top 20 with another cockney novelty, 'Will I What', but after his third similar single, the semi-controversial 'ton-up' novelty, 'Just For Kicks', had failed to score, Sarne realised, 'The cockney type of song can't go on and on as the bread and butter side of my career.' Sarne (his mother's maiden name was De Sarne), who was once an understudy to Bob Monkhouse in *Cinderella*, saw singing solely as a stepping stone towards his real ambition, film production, and when the hits stopped he put all his energy into fulfilling that ambition. By the end of the 1960s he had produced a handful of movies including the Raquel Welch and Mae West film *Myra Breckenridge* (1969). Incidentally, Wendy (who later starred in the hit TV series *Are You Being Served?* and *EastEnders*) unsuccessfully re-recorded 'Come Outside' with Mike Berry in 1986.

JOHN BARRY

York-born, trumpeter/band leader/ musical arranger/composer Barry was one of the most successful people to emerge from the early British rock'n'roll scene. He was demobbed in 1956, and after writing a few scores for Jack Parnell's Orchestra he formed the John Barry Seven. In early 1957 they appeared with visiting US acts

Mitchell Torok and Johnnie Ray. They became regulars on *6.5 Special* and were later seen on *Oh Boy!* and *Drumbeat*. Their first single was 'Zip Zip' in 1957 on Parlophone, but this and several other early records failed to click. In 1959 he teamed with fellow *Drumbeat* regular Adam Faith, and it was his string arrangements that made Faith's records so distinctive. His first film work came courtesy of Faith's movie *Beat Girl* in 1959. His own biggest hits were 'Hit And Miss' in 1960, 'Walk Don't Run' in 1961, and the theme from the TV series *The Persuaders* nine years later. Barry, whose first compositions included 'We All Love To Rock' and 'Rock-a-Billy Boogie', has since become one of the most in-demand film score writers in the world, penning numerous James Bond themes as well as the incidental music from such acclaimed movies as *Born Free*, *Midnight Cowboy*, *King Kong*, *Out of Africa*, *Dances With Wolves* and *Chaplin*.

KEITH KELLY

After spending three years in the RAF, Yorkshireman Keith Kelly joined the John Barry Seven in 1956. Three years later, and with countless TV appearances behind him, the singer/songwriter/guitarist decided the time was right to branch out as a solo artist. George Martin signed him to Parlophone Records and his career got off to an auspicious start when both sides of his debut single, 'Tease Me' and 'Ooh-La-La', entered the Top 30. However it was to be the start of something small, since his next two singles sold only moderately well, and in 1961 his last record for Parlophone, the controversial 'Cold White And Beautiful' (a song about suicide and corpse-finding sung to the tune of 'Early One Morning'), was not received warmly by the public.

SHANE FENTON & THE FENTONES

The Fentones were originally known as The Tremolos, and featured singer Johnny Theakstone, who performed under the name Shane Fenton. The 17-year-old Theakstone became terminally ill, but before he died he asked Nottingham-based Bernard Jewry to take over his stage name and group. The group became very popular locally and used the money they earned to build up an impressive wardrobe of showy stage gear. Even before their first hit, Fenton proudly announced: 'I've got 20 suits, ranging from green to gold lamé and leopard skin.' Early in 1961 they became regulars on *Saturday Club* and *Easy Beat* and were soon signed to Parlophone by producer Ron Richards. Their biggest hit was their debut release, 'I'm A Moody Guy', coupled with a praiseworthy beat revival of the hoary old chestnut, 'Five Foot Two, Eyes of Blue'. The group, who were introduced on *Thank Your Lucky Stars* as

On his debut US tour in 1960, Cliff Richard appeared on a bill with R&B greats The Isley Brothers and Clyde McPhatter

Never one to go easy on the glitter, it was almost inevitable that Shane Fenton should resurface in the Glam Rock era of the early Seventies

protégés of Helen Shapiro, also had a minor hit with a cover of 'Cindy's Birthday' in 1962. The Fentones, who consisted of Mickey Eyre (rhythm guitar), Jerry Wilcox (lead guitar), Tony Hinchcliffe (drums) and William 'Bonney' Oliver (bass), had moderate success with 'The Mexican' and 'The Breeze And I' in 1962. When asked about his choice of songs to record, Fenton replied, 'There are not many great new songs around, and the really good new material goes only to the established big names, like Cliff Richard.' In 1973 Fenton again took the stage-name of another singer, Alvin Stardust (the original vocalist being Pete Shelley), and went on to become one of that decade's top recording artists.

An atmospheric studio shot of Jet Harris and his group The Jetblacks

JET HARRIS

Bass player Terence 'Jet' Harris (nicknamed for his running ability at school) hails from Middlesex. After exchanging the clarinet for the bass guitar, he played in Terry Dene's Dene-Aces, Wee Willie Harris' combo and The Vipers Skiffle Group before joining Cliff Richard's group, The Shadows, in 1958. Harris, who penned the group's early single 'Jet Black', was, according to member Bruce Welch, 'the Shadows' official spokesman', and was the only member (in their early days) who signed contracts. Harris left the group in April 1962, as 'Wonderful Land' was topping the chart. He charted with his debut disc, the Mexican standard 'Besame Mucho', and both sides of the follow-up, 'Main Title' (an Elmer Bernstein composition that he had previously tried to persuade The Shadows to record), and the vocal, 'Some People'. When he teamed with another ex-Shadow, Tony Meehan, he added a further three Top 10 singles to his tally. Harris, a controversial figure, known for his moodiness and haunted by the idea he wouldn't live beyond 30, was very badly injured in a car crash at the end of 1963, which virtually brought to an end his recording career.

JERRY LORDAN

This London-born singer/songwriter first found fame as the composer of Mike Preston's 1958 US chart entry 'A House, A Car And A Wedding Ring' (Lordan was backed on his original demo of the song by the then unknown Emile Ford & The

Checkmates). In 1959 Anthony Newley had a major hit with Lordan's composition 'I've Waited So Long', and later that year Lordan recorded his debut single, 'So The Story Goes', as half of the duo Lee & Jay Elvin. When he tried to interest Parlophone in his song 'I'll Stay Single', with a view to it being recorded by one of their acts, they insisted that he record it himself for them. He did so, and after a slow start his record climbed into the Top 30 in early 1960. The equally catchy follow-up, 'Who Could Be Bluer', gave him his biggest hit. With two successive hits his future looked bright but, despite releasing some praiseworthy platters including the hook-heavy 'Ring, Write or Call', Lordan was to have no more vocal success. 'I feel very discouraged with the way my singing career has been progressing,' he said, 'I thought my follow-ups were all good records but obviously the fans didn't agree.' He then concentrated on song writing and the results of his efforts included huge hits for The Shadows ('Apache', 'Wonderful Land' and 'Atlantis'), their boss Cliff ('A Girl Like You' and 'Good Times'), ex-Shadows Jet Harris & Tony Meehan ('Diamonds' and 'Scarlet O'Hara'), and Louise Cordet ('I'm Just A Baby').

MICHAEL COX

Merseyside-born Michael Cox can thank his four younger sisters for getting him into show business. They wrote to Jack Good telling him that he should put their brother on one of his TV shows. Good auditioned Cox and was impressed enough to include him often on *Oh Boy!*, *Boy Meets Girls* and *Wham!* He signed with Decca in 1959 and his first recording was the Pomus & Shuman song 'Teenage Love'. The hit-making US songwriting duo were so impressed with Cox's version of their song that they wrote the follow-up, 'Serious', especially for him. However, neither release sold in any serious quantities. Cox's sole hit (which was also the only Top 20 hit released on the Joe Meek-owned independent label Triumph) came in 1960 with a version of the engaging hum-along song 'Angela Jones', composed by American John D. Loudermilk. His follow-up, an original song, 'Along Came Caroline', which had more than a passing resemblance to his previous single, narrowly missed the Top 30 and several later releases on HMV and Parlophone failed to push Cox up the chart.

GARRY MILLS

Teenage pop singer Garry Mills hailed from Surrey and was the nephew of jazz trumpeter Nat Gonella. Like so many other singers of the era he was spotted singing at London's 2 I's coffee bar, which led to his signing with Dick Rowe at Top Rank. Among his early unrewarding releases were covers of Johnny Preston's 'Running

Coffee bar decor wasn't just limited to potted plants and pictures of pop stars

The Big Chance was the name of a Jack Good TV talent show that never got past the pilot stage

Bear', Mark Dinning's death disc 'Teen Angel' and Paul Evans' 'Seven Little Girls'. His only major hit came in 1960 with 'Look For A Star', a song that appeared in the X-rated Hammer film *Circus of Horrors*, after being rejected for inclusion in Norman Wisdom's *Follow a Star*. In the States Gary's (he dropped one 'r' for the US) version was joined in the charts by three American cover versions (the most successful being by the similarly named Gary Miles!). The record was not only his biggest success, it was also the first hit for composer Mark Anthony (better known as Tony Hatch). Mills, who was backed on the road by The Flee-Rekkers, narrowly missed the Top 20 with 'Top Teen Baby' later in 1960, and can be seen in the long-forgotten films *London Nights* and *Treasure Island, W.C.2*.

KARL DENVER

Karl Denver, who was born Angus McKenzie in Glasgow, may not have looked like a typical teen idol, but he was an incredibly versatile singer with a very flexible voice. He reportedly jumped ship in America while en route back to Britain from fighting in Korea with the Argyll & Sutherland Highlanders and, according to him, spent over three years working the C&W music circuit in America (including appearances on *Grand Ol' Opry*) before being caught and deported. Denver made his TV debut on Granada's *Band Stand* in 1959. He was spotted by Jack Good when singing in a Manchester pub, and in early 1961 Good added Denver's group to a tour that starred Jess Conrad. The Karl Denver Trio appeared (in the 'new discovery' spot) in the last edition of *Wham!* and were soon regulars on BBC radio's top shows *Easy Beat* and *Saturday Club*. His debut disc, 'Marcheta', duly charted, as did his yodelling update of Bing Crosby's 1938 success, 'Mexicali Rose'. The crowd-pleasing performer followed those hits with his best-remembered record, 'Wimoweh', and very soon afterwards with his entry for the 1962 Eurovision Song Contest, 'Never Goodbye'. When that song was unplaced in the UK heat (Ronnie Carroll's 'Say Wonderful Things' was first), many critics felt the record was dead. Denver disagreed, saying, 'I certainly wouldn't describe it as a throwaway, and feel that once "Wimoweh" peaks, it could be a hit.' He was right, and 'Never Goodbye' also climbed into the Top 10. The last of Denver's five successive Top 20 entries came with a revival of the 1912 French song 'A Little Love, A

It could be tough at the top!
Karl Denver (left) and the boys (Kevin Neill and Gerry Cottrell) warming themselves around a one-bar electric fire in their manager's office

Little Kiss'. The nostalgia value of the Karl Denver Trio has continued to remain bankable since the days when they scored their nine Top 30 hits. In 1989 Denver re-recorded the African anthem 'Wimoweh' with The Happy Mondays, and a year later this unique performer's single 'Lazyitis', recorded with that same Manchester band, narrowly missed the Top 40.

RICKY VALANCE

Singer Ricky Valance (real name David Spencer) came from Ynysddu, South Wales, and his first foray into the pop firmament in 1960, 'Tell Laura I Love Her', topped the chart. The song, about a boy who dies in a stock-car race while trying to win enough money to wed Laura, caused great controversy, and it was wrongly assumed that the BBC would ban it. The pre-release publicity, and especially the withdrawal of Ray Peterson's original version, helped Valance's Norrie Paramor-produced cover to race to the top. When questioned about his choice of song and stage name (which many thought to be too similar to the recently deceased US rocker Ritchie Valens), Valance commented, 'I like story songs, and I don't think this one's in bad taste - it is very moving. As for my name, I have always been nicknamed Ricky, and liked the name Valance when I heard it on a TV programme.' Valance, who had sung briefly with the Sid Phillips Band and done a little male modelling, added, 'I like up-tempo rock songs, but I feel more at home with ballads.' Like Tommy, the hero in his hit song, Valance's career was short-lived; his other singles (including a cover of another US death disc, Neil Scott's 'Bobby') got left at the starting line.

In the days before smoking was frowned upon, a cigarette could be a useful prop in photo sessions, as in this moody study of Eden Kane

Eden Kane

EDEN KANE

Born Richard Sarstedt in Delhi, India, Eden Kane's first musical experience was in a skiffle group formed with his brothers Peter and Robin, who later both had Top 3 hits in their own right. In 1960 Kane (the surname was inspired by Orson Welles' film *Citizen Kane*) won a recording contract with Pye in a talent competition, and he so impressed one of the judges, Michael Barclay, that he signed him for management. His first single was a Cadbury's commercial, 'Hot Chocolate Baby', but it proved not to be everybody's cup of tea. Kane then joined Decca, and in 1961 his next release, 'Well I Ask You', which had been especially written for him by hit song-writer Johnny Worth (under the name Les Vandyke), soon took the 19-year-old to the top spot; its similar-sounding follow-up, 'Get Lost', also found its way into the Top 10. In an attempt to escape being musically typecast, Kane dropped his growling trademark on his next single, 'Forget Me Not' (which he considered to be the best song Johnny Worth had ever written), saying, 'With this record I hope I can obliterate the fallacy that I am essentially a growler. I only growled on the first two hits because it suited the songs.' Both 'Forget Me Not' and his revival of Wayne King's 1931 hit ,'I Don't Know Why' (which had been a US Top 20 single a few months earlier by Linda Scott), also climbed into the Top 10, elevating him to superstar status. However, it was to be a further 18 months before he returned to the chart, with the haunting and memorable 'Boys Cry' on Fontana. This single's success in Australia helped persuade Kane to head down under when succeeding follow-up singles stiffed in Britain. In later years he teamed unsuccessfully on record with his hit-making brothers, worked as an estate agent in Beverly Hills, California, and was a familiar face on the 'oldies' circuit.

DOUG SHELDON

This London-born actor/beat singer first appeared in public as a fairground barker-cum-bingo-caller in his father's Skegness fairground. After national service he managed to get a part in the hit film *The Guns Of Navarone*, and he was also seen in TV shows, including *Probation Officer* and *Something Old, Something New*. He was spotted singing in the latter show by manager Bunny Lewis, who arranged for him to join Decca. Sheldon spent months rehearsing his debut single, 'The Book Of Love' (not the Monotones/Mudlarks hit), before going into the studio, saying, 'I had the awful feeling that the session could make or break me.' It failed to chart; but the follow-up, a cover of Dion's US chart-topper, 'Runaround Sue', gave him his sole Top 20 entry in 1961. Sheldon, who was one of Decca Records producer Dick Rowe's top priority acts at the time he turned down The Beatles, narrowly missed adding to his hit tally with fairly faithful covers of Kenny Dino's hypnotic 'Your Ma Said You Cried In Your Sleep Last Night' and Dickey Lee's 'I Saw Linda Yesterday'.

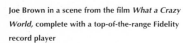

Joe Brown in a scene from the film *What a Crazy World,* complete with a top-of-the-range Fidelity record player

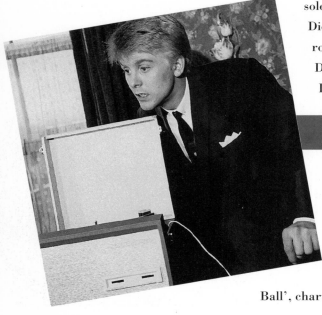

JOE BROWN

The amiable singer/guitarist with the blond, spiky crew-cut was born in Lincolnshire, but is regarded as much a part of London as Big Ben. Jack Good, who signed Brown & The Bruvvers as the backing band on *Boy Meets Girls* in 1959, realised Brown's potential and gave him his own spot on the show, and the cheerful cockney soon became very popular. Brown's second Decca single, 'Darktown Strutters Ball', charted in 1960, but despite releasing top grade rockin' revivals of the 1910

Music Hall favourite 'I'm Henry The Eighth, I Am' (a US chart topper in 1965 for Herman's Hermits) and the 1926 song 'Shine', as well as the equally catchy cockney songs 'Jellied Eels' (penned by Lionel Bart) and 'What A Crazy World We're Living In', his first major hit came only when he changed his style and recorded 'A Picture of You' in 1962. 'I guess I'd like to have made it with a rock number', Brown said, 'but if this new style is all right with the fans, then it's all right with me.' His fans took the record to No. 1, and over the next nine months Brown had two more Top 10 singles, 'It Only Took A Minute' (composed by Burt Bacharach's co-writer Hal David) and the highly contagious 'That's What Love Will Do', which was written for him by Trevor Peacock and was covered in America by Bobby Goldsboro. Brown, whose guitar work can be heard on Billy Fury's classic album The Sound Of Fury, starred in the film of *What a Crazy World* in 1963, by which time the pop world had gone group crazy, leaving no room in the Top 20 for him. However, Brown, who once topped the bill over The Beatles, and played on George Harrison's 1982 album Gone Troppo, has always kept busy and has recorded on several labels since the early 1960s. In 1989 his daughter Sam also reached the Top 5, but her hits, like dad's, have (at least temporarily) stopped.

Among US covers of Shadows hits were 'Man Of Mystery' by Chet Atkins and 'The Savage' by The Ventures

Bright and breezy, Mike Berry's image seemed slightly out of synch with having a backing group called the Outlaws

MIKE BERRY

Berry, a London born singer/actor (real name Michael Bourne), originally fronted a group called Kenny Lord & The Statesmen. Joe Meek renamed him and produced his debut disc for Decca, a Buddy Holly-influenced version of The Shirelles US chart-topper 'Will You Love Me Tomorrow'. In 1961 Berry's heartfelt 'Tribute To Buddy Holly' on HMV only narrowly missed the Top 20. The song was given the seal of approval by Holly's parents, Holly's producer Norman Petty and reputedly by Holly himself at a seance (Holly supposedly thanked writer Geoff Goddard for the honour and said 'See you in the charts'). Incidentally, this tribute record was released (unsuccessfully) in the United States by Holly's old label, Coral. The backing on this and other early Berry recordings was by The Outlaws, a noted group who included Ritchie Blackmore (later of Deep Purple) and Chas Hodges (who became successful in Chas & Dave). Berry scored his biggest hit in 1963 with 'Don't You Think It's Time', again written by spiritualist and songwriter Geoff Goddard and produced by Joe Meek. In the 1970s Berry became a well-known television actor, appearing in programmes like *Worzel Gummidge*; then, in 1980, after a 17-year gap, he returned to the Top 10 with 'The Sunshine Of Your Smile', produced by ex-Outlaw Chas Hodges.

GEOFF GODDARD

A singer/songwriter and pianist from Reading who graduated from London's Royal Academy of Music in 1959, Goddard started his musical career by playing Russ Conway-style piano in a pub, often featuring his own compositions. His first recorded song was 'Lone Rider' by The Flee-Rekkers, and fame came when John Leyton recorded his 'Johnny Remember Me' in 1961. Goddard, who was a spiritualist, claimed regular contact (through seances) with Buddy Holly. 'Buddy said he would help me, and soon after that I started getting better ideas,' Goddard explained, adding that Holly helped him with his writing and was a constant inspiration. According to Goddard, Holly said of 'Johnny Remember Me', 'It is a great song, it will go to No. 1 in the charts and be the start of good things for you.' Goddard, who also penned Leyton's other three Top 20 entries, was 'told' by Holly to sing himself and the first result of this was 'Girl Bride', in 1961, which Goddard launched on *Thank Your Lucky Stars* (introduced by John Leyton as his 'tip for the top'). It was one of the catchiest and most commercial singles of the year yet somehow failed to give one of the more unusual and most talented characters on the UK record scene the vocal hit he deserved.

Frank Ifield: not since the heady days of Ronnie Ronalde had the art of yodelling enjoyed such a high profile in the Hit Parade

FRANK IFIELD

Coventry-born Frank Ifield emigrated to Australia at the age of nine, and within six years had his own radio and TV show there. After making a name for himself down under, he headed back to Britain in 1959 and signed to Columbia. Ifield briefly visited the Top 30 in 1960 with his interpretation of Carl Dobkins Jr.'s US Top 40 entry 'Lucky Devil' and, in mid-1962, a revival of Jimmy Dorsey's 1942 success 'I Remember You' took him to top of the chart. Within 12 months he had amassed another three No. 1 singles: 'Lovesick Blues' (a 1949 hit for Hank Williams), which became his second UK million seller, 'Wayward Wind' (a US No. 1 for Gogi Grant in 1956) and 'Confessin' (Guy Lombardo's 1930 success). For a while it looked as if this singer, with the distinctive falsetto and yodel, would be unaffected by the beat group boom; however, by the time the British Invasion of the States started in 1964, Ifield's popularity had peaked and his golden goose had become egg-bound. The country-influenced performer has been a regular rider on the nostalgia bandwagon ever since, which gives his loyal fans the chance to let him know 'I remember you-oo'.

KENNY LYNCH

London-born Kenny Lynch, OBE, who has been a top television personality for three decades, is one of Britain's best known black all-round entertainers. He is the youngest of 13 children, and first appeared on stage with his sister, singer Maxine Daniels, when he was 12. Before going into the services in 1957 Lynch sang with various bands including those of Bob Miller and Ed Nichols. He signed to HMV in 1960 and his debut single, a cover of rockabilly artist Harold Dorman's 'Mountain Of Love', only narrowly missed the Top 30. In 1962, he charted with 'Puff (Up In Smoke)', and had the biggest UK hit version of The Drifters' American Top 5 record 'Up On The Roof'. The singer/songwriter, who also appeared in several films, returned to the Top 10 in 1963 with a catchy song co-written with Ian Samwell, 'You Can Never Stop Me Loving You' (which became a US Top 20 hit when covered by Johnny Tillotson). Lynch, who also co-wrote the Small Faces' 1966 No. 1 'Sha La La La Lee', had a surprise chart return in 1983 with a Brit-funk track 'Half The Day's Gone And We Haven't Earned A Penny'.

Kenny Lynch – a genuine 'all-rounder', he became part of the show business establishment

JIMMY JUSTICE

After seeing him singing in a coffee bar, Emile Ford brought Surrey-born Jimmy Justice (real name James Little) to the attention of Pye Records. Justice's first release in 1960 was a revival of Wynonie Harris' 1951 rhythm and blues stomper 'Bloodshot Eyes', which he followed with a double-sided cover of Virginia R&B group The Jarmels' recordings, 'Little Lonely One' and 'Little Bit Of Soap'. When these singles failed to make any impact in the United Kingdom, Justice relocated to Sweden where 'Little Lonely One' had made the charts. In 1962, with the help of producer Tony Hatch, he scored three successive UK Top 30 hits: 'When My Little Girl Is Smiling', 'Ain't That Funny', written for him by Johnny Worth, and the Leiber and Stoller classic 'Spanish Harlem'. He spent 1962 commuting between Sweden (where he had previous bookings to honour) and Britain where, together with his group the Excheckers (which included ex-members of Emile Ford's Checkmates and The Brook Brothers' backing band, The Semi-Tones), he joined a Larry Parnes package tour headed by Billy Fury and Joe Brown. In many ways he was just a little bit ahead of his time, the tranatlantic sound he emulated was going to take another year or so to permeate into the broad pop consciousness. Unfortunately, this white rhythm and blues influenced singer, who was sometimes called 'Britain's Ben E. King', boarded a boat to oblivion just as R&B's ship was coming in.

Surf and Smiles

Early Sixties US Pop

In many critical reviews of the era, 1959 is recalled as the year rock went into a coma in America, only to be revived by The Beatles in 1964. Ever since Charlie Gillett's excellent ground-breaking book, *Sound Of The City* (to which this author contributed), first criticised certain Philadelphia performers for diluting rock, it has been fashionable to lay the blame for the demise of rock'n'roll at the door of acts like Frankie Avalon, Fabian, Freddy Cannon and Bobby Rydell. If you believed everything you may have read on the subject, you could not be blamed for thinking that Avalon's recording of 'Venus' was the first pop ballad sung by a teen idol in the rock era, which was obviously not the case.

Bobby Vee was a prominent example of the clean-cut school of American pop stars in the early Sixties, who also infiltrated the British charts to a considerable degree. Between 1961 and '63 he had no less than seven UK Top Ten entries, including 'Rubber Ball', 'Take Good Care Of My Baby' and 'The Night Has A Thousand Eyes'

In 1956, for every 'Long Tall Sally' and 'Heartbreak Hotel', there was an 'I'll Be Home' or a 'Love Me Tender'; in 1957, for every 'School Day' or ' Great Balls Of Fire', there was a 'Love Letters in The Sand' or a 'Young Love'; and in 1958, for every 'Sweet Little 16' and 'Good Golly Miss Molly', there was an 'All I Have To Do Is Dream' or a 'Don't' - in other words, rock and ballads always lived side by side. You can take it as gospel that average late-1950s record buyers did not see themselves as either out and out rock fanatics or as ballad lovers. They brought a mixture of both styles, and liked them equally well. For the record, the class of '59 produced some of rock's finest moments, including Lloyd Price's 'Stagger Lee', Ray Charles' 'What'd I Say' and Philadelphian Freddy Cannon's 'Tallahassee Lassie'. As for the fables of Fabian, few would disagree with the view that, like Tab Hunter earlier, he was more of a looker than a singer, but recordings like 'I'm A Man', 'Turn Me Loose' and 'Tiger' had a good feel, and were among the best of the rock hits of 1959. Avalon, who was talented enough to be signed by RCA before he had even reached his teens, sold millions of records in America in 1959 and temporarily replaced Elvis (who was in the army at the time) as the most successful chart artist of the year, with Lloyd Price and Paul Anka being his nearest rivals.

In the early 1960s popular mythology has it that a brigade of well-groomed Bobbys (Darin, Rydell, Vee & Vinton) joined the photogenic Philadelphia pretenders to the rock'n'roll throne, and together they stifled all good rocking music until The Beatles bobbed up. The fact is that many teenage record buyers had simply tired of raw rock by 1960 and wanted the style of music that *Billboard* tagged Teen Beat — they actually liked a little more glitz and a little less grits in their hits.

In 1960 Elvis returned from the army, and took back the crown for top artist of the year. Brenda Lee and Connie Francis filled out the Top 3, and Mr. Rydell in fourth place was the biggest 'Bobby'. In 1961, Elvis let the ladies go first, and both Brenda Lee and R&B quartet The Shirelles out-pointed him, whilst Mr. Vee fronted the bunch of Bobbys. In 1962, when the Twist rejuvenated teen beat, Chubby Checker was America's top artist, Elvis was runner-up and Ray Charles was placed third.

This brings us to the last year that US artists totally dominated their own Top 100. The usual story of those pre-Beatles days ends by suggesting that by 1963 the American music scene was stagnant, ballad-heavy, boring and badly in need of a transfusion of new young blood from Britain. In reality it was a very diverse and interesting year for American pop music. It was the year when surf music rode the crest of a wave and when folk music found a new social awareness, thanks to Bob Dylan, whose debut album appeared in 1962, and his brand of protest songs. If there was any lack of excitement in the year's music, it was not the fault of the R&B end of the rock spectrum which accounted for nearly 40% of singles sales. The music of the Afro-American performers who followed in the footsteps of rock greats like Little Richard, Fats Domino and Chuck Berry was equally as exciting and vibrant as that of their predecessors. Motown came of age in 1963, with acts like Stevie Wonder, Marvin Gaye and The Supremes debuting on the pop charts. James Brown and The Miracles reached new heights and dance crazes such as the Monkey, Dog and Bird came out of black America to replace the Twist. It was the year when 18-year-old Lesley Gore and the Beach Boys were the chart champs, and veteran rock star Dion, just out-pointed folk trio Peter, Paul & Mary for third place. Perhaps this very diversity was a pointer to the fact that America was ready to be engulfed by a new musical trend.

However, even though Britain was experiencing its first year of the Group Invasion, there was still room in the UK Top 30 for 52 of America's Top 20 hits of 1963. In other words, 30% of the USA's biggest hits repeated their success in Britain in the first year of The Beatles' chart domination. This was an increase on the previous year and not that far short of America's best performance in Britain. This, coupled with the fact that the majority of British hits were still being written by American songwriters, suggests that far from being a spent force in 1963 (as is sometimes opined by critics), the US was still very much on the ball when it came to the needs of transatlantic record buyers.

The first two acts to top the US singles and album charts simultaneously were Stevie Wonder (age 13) and The Singing Nun!

Fabian never emulated his American success in the UK, where his title hit from the film *Hound Dog Man* just scraped into the Top 50

A theory worth considering is that America's new generation of white adolescents desperately needed teen idols they could call their own. In 1963 fans were starting to get the seven year itch with Elvis (whose output of songs was getting weaker), Frankie Avalon and Fabian were yesterday's news, Paul Peterson had peaked and the Bobbys – Rydell, Darin and Vee – as well as Ricky Nelson (another singer who looked better than he sang - yet one who most critics consider credible) were fast losing their fan bases. Dion was selling stacks of singles (mainly with timely revivals of R&B material), but had been a pin up for six years, and teens never like to share their older sisters' idols. Surfer boys like the photogenic Jan & Dean, and the not so photogenic Beach Boys were making the pages of the teen mags but surf music, possibly due to its lyrical content, appealed more to the older teenager. There was therefore definitely room in the lives of pubescent teenagers for singers with basic teen idol qualifications: good looks, good music, teen-slanted lyrics and possibly an appearance that would, at least initially, worry parents.

The Beach Boys started their run of surf hits in 1962 with 'Surfin' Safari' and were the first hint Stateside of group-mania to come

To summarise the situation just prior to The Beatles' phenomenal arrival on American shores, there was a definite shortage of white teen idols (in those pre-Michael Jackson years, few pictures of black stars found their way onto white teenagers' walls) and R&B aimed primarily at black audiences was the source of the most exciting music. The scene had several similarities to that of 1955 – America was ready for another good looking, slightly controversial white act who had received their shots of rhythm & blues. In early 1956, that description fitted Elvis; in early 1964 it suited The Beatles.

For those who doubt that The Beatles were from the R&B school of rock music, check out their early repertoire and you will find songs like Little Willie John's 'Leave My Kitten Alone', Chuck Berry's 'Sweet Little Sixteen', 'Memphis' and 'Little Queenie,' Arthur Alexander's 'Where Have You Been (All My Life)', Little Richard's 'Kansas City' and 'Long Tall Sally', The Coasters' 'Searchin' and 'Three Cool Cats' and Richie Barrett's 'Some Other Guy' to name but a few. If that's not enough proof, remember that nearly half of the tracks on their first couple of albums were covers of R&B songs (the same had also been true of Elvis, and was also true of the Rolling Stones). To quote Little Richard who toured with them in 1962, 'Honestly, if I hadn't seen them with my own eyes I'd have thought they were a coloured group from back home.'

Backroom Boys

THE POP PRODUCTION LINE

Dave Lane of The Mudlarks said, 'Occasionally we didn't even have time to rehearse or learn how to phrase the songs we were given to record'

Behind every hit record (and indeed every flop) there is always a big team of 'backroom boys'. This is as true in this technological recording age as it was in the early days of rock'n'roll. Numbered among the behind-the-scenes team for each release are the producer, song writers, musical arranger, studio engineer, session musicians, background vocalists, A&R man, manager, agent and the staff at the record company and music publishers concerned. To mention even briefly all the people who contributed, in their own way, to the hits of the pre-Beat Boom years would be an impossible task in anything smaller than an encyclopedia. However, this book would not be complete without at least looking at the careers of ace songwriters like Johnny Worth and Lionel Bart, Britain's premier rock'n'roll manager Larry Parnes, TV producer Jack Good and the leading UK record producers of the period, including Norrie Paramor, George Martin and the now-legendary Joe Meek.

JOHNNY WORTH

London-born singer/songwriter Johnny Worth of Greek-Cypriot extraction - his real name is Yani Paraskos Paraskeva Skordalides - was spotted while singing in a pub in Cheam. This led to his appearing on BBC's youth-oriented show, *Teleclub*, in 1953. The programme was seen by Oscar Rabin, who recruited him as his band's vocalist, a position he held for five years. In 1957 (while still with Rabin) Worth signed with Woolworth's budget label Embassy (who released double-sided cover-version singles at a budget price) as a solo artist. He joined vocal group The Raindrops in 1958 and his first recorded composition, 'Italian Style', was cut by them as a B-side a year later. His big break came when fellow *Drumbeat* regular Adam Faith's

Eden Kane was one of the impressive roster of acts who charted with Johnny Worth compositions

recording of Worth's 1957 composition, 'What Do You Want', shot to the top in 1959. Apart from composing (usually under the name Les Vandyke) other Faith hits, including the Top 5 entries 'Someone Else's Baby', 'As You Like It', 'How About That' and 'The Time Has Come' and the chart-topping 'Poor Me', his catalogue of chart entries included Eden Kane's Top 10 hits 'Well I Ask You', 'Get Lost' and 'Forget Me Not'. Also among Worth's impressive inventory of hits in the early 1960s were 'Ain't That Funny' for Jimmy Justice, 'Applejack' for Jet Harris & Tony Meehan, 'Cupboard Love' for John Leyton, and Anthony Newley's 'Bee Bom' (often quoted as a favourite of President Kennedy). Incidentally, as a vocalist Worth recorded a version on Embassy of 'It Doesn't Matter Any More' (the Buddy Holly song that the arrangement of 'What Do You Want' was based on), and even released faithful covers of his own compositions 'What Do You Want', 'Someone Else's Baby', 'Poor Me' and 'How About That'. The closest he ever came to charting as a singer was probably his 1962 recording 'You Know What I Mean', which was produced for him by Adam Faith.

LIONEL BART

Lionel Bart 'relaxes at home' with his records in this carefully-posed 'informal' publicity shot

This-London born tunesmith (real name Lionel Begleiter) initially came to the public's attention as co-writer of the first British rock'n'roll record to make the Top 20, 'Rock With The Caveman' by Tommy Steele. Apart from co-writing other Steele hits including 'Handful Of Songs', 'Water Water', 'Butterfingers' and 'Little White Bull', Bart also penned the chart toppers 'Living Doll' for Cliff Richard in 1959 (which returned to the top 27 years later performed by Cliff and The Young Ones) and 'Do You Mind' for Anthony Newley in 1960. He also composed such hits as 'Easy Going Me' and 'When Johnny Comes Marching Home' for Adam

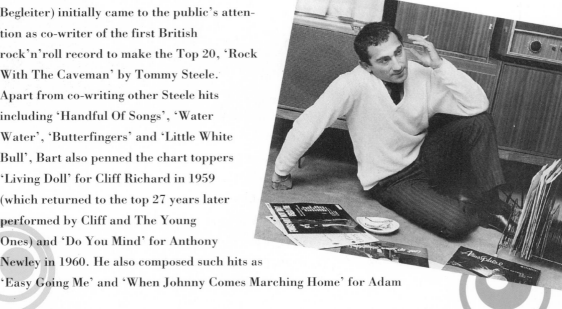

Faith, 'Fings Ain't Wot They Used T'be' (the title song from his first
musical), a Top 5 hit for Max Bygraves in 1960 and 'From Russia With
Love' for Matt Monro. However, Bart is probably best remembered as the
writer of the international hit musical *Oliver*, which includes the oft-heard
'Consider Yourself', 'I'd Do Anything' and 'As Long As He Needs Me',
which became a Top 3 hit in 1960 for Shirley Bassey. After a comparatively
lean period, when he suffered personal and financial problems, Bart
debuted in the chart as a vocalist in 1989 with 'Happy Endings'.

LARRY PARNES

The best-known and most successful manager and impresario in Britain in
the early rock era was undoubtedly Londoner Larry Parnes. In 1956 publi-
cist John Kennedy enlisted Parnes to co-man-
age his discovery Tommy Hicks. They
renamed him Tommy Steele, put a publicity
campaign behind him, and overnight he
became Britain's first rock'n'roll star. The
next vocalist to benefit from Parnes' exper-
tise was Reg Smith (who became Marty
Wilde), and soon afterwards Ronald
Wycherley (rechristened by Parnes as
Billy Fury) joined Parnes' roster of
rockers. Parnes became a household
name in the UK, and the media liked
nothing better than to write about the
ever-expanding stable of young studs
that he was grooming for stardom. By
the end of the 1950s his herd of
would-be Hit Parade Heroes included Joe
Brown, Vince Eager, Georgie Fame, Lance Fortune, Johnny Gentle,
Duffy Power and Dickie Pride, none of whom were getting the chart success
of his first three signings. Parnes (like Alan Freed in the US) always seemed
to have at least one all-star package show on the road, and these shows
inevitably played to large and enthusiastic crowds in cinemas and theatres
across Britain. In the early 1960s Larry Parnes concentrated his efforts on
this side of the business, and was the promoter behind most of the successful
rock tours at the time (including the ill-fated Gene Vincent & Eddie Cochran

Lance Fortune:
he was just one of the
discoveries of Larry
Parnes, known in the
business as 'Mr Parnes,
Shillings and Pence'

tour of 1960). When he died in 1989 an obituary to him in the American magazine *Billboard* said: 'Larry Parnes' stable of artists changed forever the face and sound of UK pop.'

JACK GOOD

Jack Good's name probably appears more often in this book than anyone else's. Good, a London-born, ex-Oxford University student recalled, 'I went to see the film *Rock Around the Clock* - the music was fantastic and the kids were bopping about in the aisles - I was converted like St. Paul on the way to Damascus.' He became the No. 1 ally of rock'n'roll on British television. He produced (with Josephine Douglas) the ground-breaking *6.5 Special* series in 1957 and, after falling out with the powers-that-be at the BBC, moved over to ITV where he produced the much-loved shows *Oh Boy!*, *Boy Meets Girls*, and *Wham!* To list the British artists who gained invaluable TV exposure on these shows would read like a Who's Who of early UK rock, and would include super-stars Cliff Richard, Marty Wilde, Adam Faith and Billy Fury. Good not only found time to produce acts like Fury, Karl Denver, Jess Conrad, and Lord Rockingham's XI, but also involved himself in r'n'r stage shows (often in conjunction with Larry Parnes). Via his television programmes and his regular and very popular column in *Disc*, Good helped influence British musical trends, and by 1962, when pop and rock had gone relatively soft, he was pointing the public towards R&B. Apart from raving about various US R&B singles, he was arguably the first R&B producer in the UK working with Blues

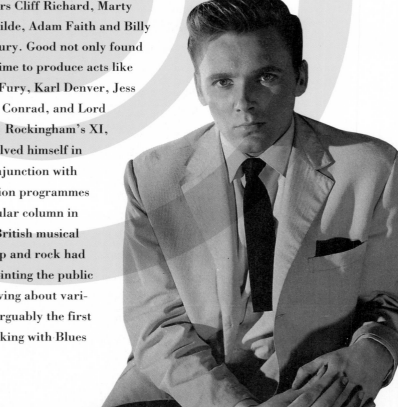

Billy Fury – one of the true Hit Parade Heroes, who found fame through Good's television shows

A poster for the film version of *6.5 Special*, the pioneering TV show created by Jack Good

Inc. and Jimmy Powell. R&B, as he predicted, was the next musical craze in the UK and gave birth to the British beat boom which was heard all around the world. Among Good's other achievements in the 1960s were the production (at their request) of The Beatles' first TV special, *Around The Beatles* in 1964, and the production of his first US TV pop series, *Shindig*, which proved to be a big success, introducing the world to such acts as Sonny & Cher and The Righteous Brothers. He has since staged the successful musicals *Elvis* and *Good Rockin' Tonite*.

NORRIE PARAMOR

Norrie Paramor, who hailed from London, was the most successful British record producer of the pre-Beatles days. In the 1930s he worked as a pianist with Gracie Fields and as an arranger for various dance bands, including that of Maurice Winnick. During the war years Paramor was musical director for Ralph Reader's *Gang Show* and wrote arrangements for acts like Noel Coward and Mantovani. He played the piano in Harry Gold's noted band in 1944-9, then left to concentrate on arranging. Paramor made his first record for Columbia in 1950 (accompanying Marie Benson - later of The Stargazers), and by 1952 was a director of the label. Although never a great fan of rock music, during 1954-69 he produced no less than 27 UK No. 1 hits, which included records by Eddie Calvert, Michael Holliday, Frank Ifield, Ruby Murray, Cliff Richard, The Scaffold, The Shadows, Helen Shapiro and Ricky Valance. He also produced hits for British acts The Avons, Tommy Bruce, Tony Brent, Tony Crombie & The Rockets (Britain's first rock'n'roll artists on record) and The Mudlarks as well as being at the controls for the first solo single recorded by American teenage sensation Frankie Lymon. As a composer Paramor (who wrote under an amazing 34 pseudonyms) penned hits for Acker Bilk ('Lonely'), Billy Fury ('Once Upon A Dream'), Cliff Richard ('A Voice In The Wilderness'), The Shadows ('Frightened City' and 'The Savage') and Helen Shapiro ('Let's Talk About Love'), as well as numerous B-sides and

Looking a generation behind the scene he unwittingly helped create, Norrie Paramor

music used in films such as *It's Trad, Dad!*, *Expresso Bongo* and *The Young Ones*. He scored his biggest hits as a recording artist under the nom-de-disque of the Big Ben Banjo Band, whose medley single 'Let's Get Together No. 1' reached the Top 10 in 1955. Paramor died in 1979, still holding the UK record for producing the most Number Ones.

GEORGE MARTIN

When The Beatles first met George Martin (below) what impressed John Lennon most was the fact that he'd worked with ex-*Goon Show* stars Peter Sellers and Spike Milligan

Many people mistakenly assume that George Martin's first claim to real fame was his work with The Beatles. In reality Martin had been the head of A&R for Parlophone Records since 1955 (having previously been Oscar Preuss' assistant at the label). In January 1956 he had three of his productions simultaneously in the UK Top 20, the artists involved being TV personality Eamonn Andrews, vocalist Eve Boswell and ballad singer Dick James, who a few years later (as publisher of The Beatles) would again work closely with him. Martin also handled production duties for such diverse acts as Johnny Dankworth, The Vipers skiffle group, Jimmy Shand's traditional Scottish dance band, Matt Monro, Jim Dale, Keith Kelly, the zany Temperance Seven and funny men Peter Sellers, Flanders & Swann, Bernard Cribbins, Peter Ustinov, Charlie Drake and Spike Milligan. 'People tell me there's no future in recording comedians,' Martin said in the late 1950s, 'and my greatest pleasure is proving them wrong.' Although not initially a fan of rock music (he turned down Tommy Steele among others), he was one of the first producers to realise that rock was here to stay, and thereafter kept his door open to rock acts, especially if they wrote their own material. He, too, credited his supporting cast, which included musical arrangers Ron Goodwin and Ken Jones, for much of his success, and when questioned in 1959 about the type of act he was looking for said, 'It's not so much artistry but individuality that counts today.' In 1962 Martin was described by the *NME* as 'The man who has done more than anyone else to put British disc comedy well and truly on the map'. Only a few weeks later Liverpool record shop owner Brian Epstein walked through his door with a tape....

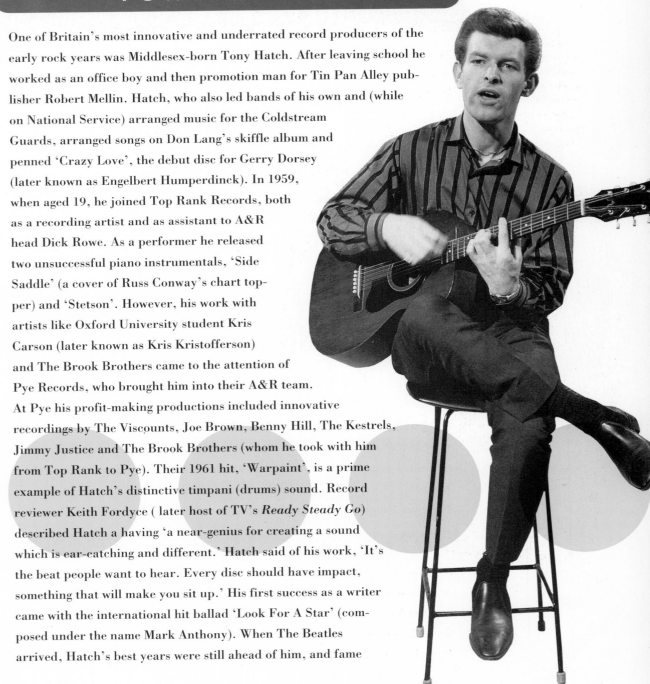

Jimmy Justice, one of the A&R successes for Pye Records' Tony Hatch

TONY HATCH

One of Britain's most innovative and underrated record producers of the early rock years was Middlesex-born Tony Hatch. After leaving school he worked as an office boy and then promotion man for Tin Pan Alley publisher Robert Mellin. Hatch, who also led bands of his own and (while on National Service) arranged music for the Coldstream Guards, arranged songs on Don Lang's skiffle album and penned 'Crazy Love', the debut disc for Gerry Dorsey (later known as Engelbert Humperdinck). In 1959, when aged 19, he joined Top Rank Records, both as a recording artist and as assistant to A&R head Dick Rowe. As a performer he released two unsuccessful piano instrumentals, 'Side Saddle' (a cover of Russ Conway's chart topper) and 'Stetson'. However, his work with artists like Oxford University student Kris Carson (later known as Kris Kristofferson) and The Brook Brothers came to the attention of Pye Records, who brought him into their A&R team. At Pye his profit-making productions included innovative recordings by The Viscounts, Joe Brown, Benny Hill, The Kestrels, Jimmy Justice and The Brook Brothers (whom he took with him from Top Rank to Pye). Their 1961 hit, 'Warpaint', is a prime example of Hatch's distinctive timpani (drums) sound. Record reviewer Keith Fordyce (later host of TV's *Ready Steady Go*) described Hatch a having 'a near-genius for creating a sound which is ear-catching and different.' Hatch said of his work, 'It's the beat people want to hear. Every disc should have impact, something that will make you sit up.' His first success as a writer came with the international hit ballad 'Look For A Star' (composed under the name Mark Anthony). When The Beatles arrived, Hatch's best years were still ahead of him, and fame came his way thanks to his production work with Petula Clark (he also penned most of her major hits) and Merseybeat group The Searchers, and his knack of writing catchy theme songs like those for the television soap operas *Crossroads* and *Neighbours*.

NORMAN NEWELL

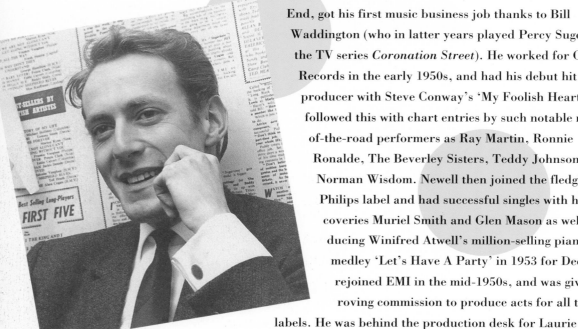

Before finding fame in Hollywood, composer and band leader John Barry was one of many hitmakers produced by Norman Newell

Producer Norman Newell, who hails from London's East End, got his first music business job thanks to Bill Waddington (who in latter years played Percy Sugden in the TV series *Coronation Street*). He worked for Columbia Records in the early 1950s, and had his debut hit as a producer with Steve Conway's 'My Foolish Heart'. He followed this with chart entries by such notable middle-of-the-road performers as Ray Martin, Ronnie Ronalde, The Beverley Sisters, Teddy Johnson and Norman Wisdom. Newell then joined the fledgling Philips label and had successful singles with his discoveries Muriel Smith and Glen Mason as well as producing Winifred Atwell's million-selling piano medley 'Let's Have A Party' in 1953 for Decca. He rejoined EMI in the mid-1950s, and was given a roving commission to produce acts for all their labels. He was behind the production desk for Laurie London's US chart-topping 'He's Got The Whole World In His Hands', pianist Russ Conway's staggering series of hits and all The King Brothers' successes. Newell also produced albums for the TV shows *6.5 Special*, *Oh Boy!* and *Drumbeat*. 1960 was a particularly good year for recording manager Newell: he clocked up 16 Top 20 hits, including a handful by Adam Faith and others by John Barry, Shirley Bassey, Russ Conway, The King Brothers, Donald Peers and American star Connie Francis.

JOE MEEK

Joe Meek from Newent, Gloucestershire, is one of the most respected British record producers of all time. After moving to London, the ex-TV repair man worked for IBC (Independent Broadcasting Company) and while there he became an engineer for Radio Luxembourg Road Shows. In 1956 he was the sound engineer (and arguably the co-producer with Denis Preston) of 'Bad Penny Blues' by Humphrey Lyttelton's Band, the single which not only gave 'Humph' his sole hit but was the first traditional jazz record to reach the Top 20. Meek soon became a much sought-after sound engineer, and in 1956-9 worked on hits like Anne Shelton's chart-topping 'Lay Down Your Arms', Frankie Vaughan's 'Green Door' and several Lonnie Donegan singles, including 'Don't You Rock Me Daddy-O' and the chart toppers 'Cumberland Gap' and 'Gamblin' Man'. He was also involved with late 1950s hits by Johnny Duncan ('Last Train To San Fernando'), Gary Miller ('Garden Of Eden') and Marty Wilde ('Sea Of Love'), plus the million sellers 'Petite Fleur' by Chris Barber's Jazz Band and 'What Do You Want To Make Those Eyes At Me For' by Emile Ford. As the decade ended his productions of 'Mr. Blue' by Mike Preston and 'Be Mine' by Lance Fortune reached the Top 20. In 1960 he launched Britain's first real independent label, Triumph, whose sole success was 'Angela Jones' by Michael Cox, and he set up a studio (RGM Sound) in his two-room flat above a shop in London's Holloway Road. His atmospheric production of 'Johnny Remember Me' by John Leyton topped the chart in 1961, and he followed this with a string of successful Leyton singles, including the Top 3 hit 'Wild Wind'. Meek, who produced outstanding (if unsuccessful) singles by Cliff Bennett & The Rebel Rousers, Screaming Lord Sutch and Geoff Goddard, had his biggest seller with the transatlantic No. 1 instrumental 'Telstar' by The Tornados in 1962, which sold over five million globally. Meek was really starting to make a name for himself when the beat boom happened, and heralded the beginning of the end for him. In 1963-4 Meek lost momentum and, despite chart appearances courtesy of records by Mike Berry & The Outlaws, Heinz, The Tornados and The Honeycombs (who scored a transatlantic Top 5 hit with the stomping 'Have I The Right'), his status in the industry steadily declined. Meek was one of the most innovative people in the British music industry in the early rock era, but his 'backroom boys', including his underrated young musical director Charles Blackwell and songwriter Geoff Goddard, should also not be forgotten when accolades are handed out. Meek, who had a premonition that Buddy Holly would die on February 3, and believed he himself would die violently before his 40th birthday, committed suicide on the anniversary of Holly's death in 1967, aged 37.

John Leyton at an *NME* Poll Winners' concert, belting out Joe Meek's production masterpiece 'Johnny Remember Me'

Whatever Next?

Northern Rumblings

In the early 1960s pop music mellowed, raw rock'n'roll merged with Tin Pan Alley pop, and the trend-setters were slicker and more polished than the wild young men who had helped give birth to rock earlier. The vast majority of transatlantic record buyers considered unrefined, rebellious rock music and its purveyors old fashioned - there was a fast-diminishing interest in these leather-bound dinosaurs. Acts who were not trendy, and did not follow the norm, were often forced to go to places like Germany (where the public appeared to be living in the past) to get record deals, and indeed to get regular work - there seemed to be no future in Britain or America's go-ahead music industry for (supposedly) retrogressive acts like The Beatles.

Some may find it inconceivable that anyone could have failed to spot the potential of the Beatles; yet most music business people who saw or heard them did just that. In Britain, apart from being rejected by Decca, the group also apparently got the thumbs down from Pye, Philips, Oriole, Columbia and HMV, and the German label Polydor, who had recorded them in 1960, did not renew their contract. Independent producer Joe Meek decided against taking them under his wing, and Larry Parnes did not consider them good enough to be Billy Fury's backing group. After being asked for a copy of the group's German release, 'My Bonnie', in late 1961, Liverpool record shop owner Brian Epstein decided to check out the local group, liked what he saw and soon after signed them to a management contract. In January 1962, 'My Bonnie' was released in the UK, as by Tony Sheridan & The Beatles, and *NME* reviewer Keith Fordyce (later host of TV's *Ready Steady Go*) said 'They are a young British group who display a welcome amount of imagination. Both sides [b-side was an update of 'The Saints'] are worth a listen for the above-average ideas.' The single was also released in the US, as by Tony Sheridan & The Beat Brothers and, although it failed to ignite any interest, no less an act than The Ventures brought out a version of the old Scottish air in competition.

Thanks to Epstein's persistence, The Beatles finally got themselves a deal with Parlophone Records, and in September went into the studio with noted novelty producer George Martin. Martin thought they would be an ideal vehicle for the catchy Mitch Murray composition 'How Do You Do It?', and Epstein agreed. The Beatles cut a lack-lustre version of the song (which would later be a chart topper for

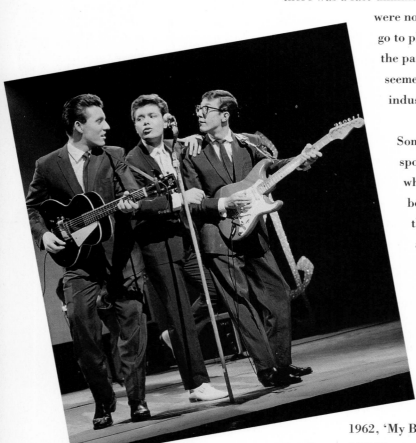

The most enduring Hit Parade Hero of them all, Cliff – with Shadows Bruce Welch (left) and Hank Marvin (right)

another Epstein group, Gerry & The Pacemakers) and insisted Martin record something they had written. It should be remembered that at the time there was an inbred feeling that UK performers could only write second division songs, and should leave song writing to either British professionals, or to Americans. Martin selected a song that members John Lennon and Paul McCartney had started writing in 1957, 'Love Me Do'. It took 17 takes (and 2 drummers), over two separate recording sessions, before Martin was satisfied. The record, which combined an R&B groove with touches of Buddy Holly and The Everly Brothers, was topped off by a harmonica solo (not unlike that on Bruce Channel's then recent hit 'Hey! Baby').

In the 'New Signings' section of the *NME* dated September 21, 1962, it mentioned below such notable new acts as 13-year-olds Sue (McGowan) & Mary (McGlynn), Chance Gordon and 16-year-old Beverley Jones, 'Liverpool group, The Beatles have recorded "Love Me Do" for Parlophone, which is set for October 5 release'. Incidentally, the major signing news that week was of blind singer Lennie Peters (his first hit came as half of Peters & Lee in 1973).

For the record, the back page of that *NME* carried an advertisement from Clayman Entertainments, listing among the acts they represented (in small print), The Searchers and The Dave Clark Five.

One of the Hit Parade Heroines, Helen Shapiro

The *Record Mirror* reviewer gave 'Love Me Do' three bells (top mark 5), saying 'the strangely named group are fairly restrained in their approach and indulge in some off-beat combinations of vocal chords. Though there's plenty happening, it tends to drag about mid-way, especially when the harmonica takes over. Not a bad song though.' Incidentally, on the day 'Love Me Do' entered the Top 30, London-based R&B band the Rolling Stones were recording their first demos.

Even after the record entered the British chart, The Beatles were unsure of the reception they would receive outside of Merseyside. McCartney confided, 'When we play outside Liverpool, as often as not we hire a couple of coaches and take an audience with us'. In an interview in November 1962 he admitted, 'A lot of people (in other areas) still don't like our music', adding that their retreads of US R&B songs like 'Some Other Guy', 'Twist & Shout' and 'If You Gotta Make A Fool Of

'Please Please Me', the Beatles' first No 1, was originally intended as the B-side of their debut single 'Love Me Do'

'Somebody' (later a hit for Freddie & The Dreamers) went down better than their original songs. He candidly admitted about these cover versions, 'We improvise on the originals - not to improve them but because we can't get the sound on the discs'.

By the time The Beatles broke in the United States, they exuded supreme confidence in themselves and their songs. However, in those early days they still lacked 100 per cent belief in their ability as songwriters. This can be clearly seen by the fact that 13 of the tracks included on their first two UK albums were covers of American recordings (mainly recent R&B hits and old rockers). It was their success and critical acclaim that gave The Beatles their real confidence.

Dusty and her fellow Springfields having received the *NME* 1961-62 Award for Top Vocal Group

The most successful British instrumental group of all time, The Shadows

Little Richard, whom the group supported on shows in late 1962, was the first American to rave in print about them, saying: 'I've never heard a sound like that before from an English group of musicians before' and adding that he would put his photo taken with the group next to the one of him with Elvis. In early 1963 they toured with American stars Chris Montez and Tommy Roe. Montez, whose collarless jackets so impressed The Beatles that they copied them, said at the time: 'As soon as I get get back to the States I'm gonna cut some of their songs – in fact, it'll be a race to see who gets them out first, Tommy Roe or me'. The Beatles were not unhappy at this prospect as they thought Montez or Roe would stand a better chance of hitting in the US than they would themselves. As it turned out, Del Shannon (who also worked with them in 1963) was the first American to cover a Beatles song, and his version of their second UK chart-topper 'From Me To You' gave Lennon and McCartney their first taste of American Top 100 success.

Even a matter of days before the release of The Beatles' second single, 'Please Please Me', the usually on-the-ball British music press seemed to have no idea how important The Beatles might be. The group, who were the 111th most successful chart act of 1962, were not mentioned by any of the music press round-ups of the year. Even more surprisingly, they were not listed alongside

the somewhat forgettable Steve Perry, Johnny De Little, Patti Lynn,
Jan Burnette and the Polka Dots in anyone's tips for 1963 success – it
appeared that no one in the music business establishment had spotted
The Beatles' potential.

In late November 1962 the *NME* announced its Poll winners for the year.
Elvis Presley was voted World's Top Male Singer, The Everly Brothers
World's Top Vocal Group with Brenda Lee World's Top Female Singer –
a clean sweep for the Americans. The British section winners included
Cliff Richard (Top Male), Helen Shapiro (Top Female), The Shadows
(Top Small Group), The Springfields (Top Vocal Group), Jet Harris
(Top Instrumentalist) and Joe Brown (Top Vocal Personality). In the
British vocal group section, just below The Vernon Girls at No. 5,
were The Beatles, and they also scraped (receiving less than 250
votes) into the Top Small Groups section at No. 8 behind Peter Jay
and The Jaywalkers.

Joe Brown, one of the memorable faces of the era
and still very active on the music scene

But there were rumblings of change – and not just from up north.
While The Beatles and other Merseyside groups were beginning to make an
impression on the world south of Birmingham, guitarist Alexis Korner was the
catalyst for an equally important revolution in the capital itself. His once-a-week
R&B sessions at the Marquee jazz club in Oxford Street were the focus for a blues
cult that was about to become a full-scale boom. As well as featuring his own band
Blues Incorporated, (which included Jack Bruce on bass and Ginger Baker on
drums) Korner played host to a young group from West London calling themselves
The Rolling Stones, who soon found themselves on a beat bandwaggon as 'London's
answer to the Beatles!'

Within a year the two-pronged assault on the pop status quo was complete. Liverpool
groups dominated the charts, while a nationwide club scene had sprung up resound-
ed to the wailing sound of guitar-and-harmonica Chicago-style blues bands.

Meanwhile back in the USA, Alan Freed, arguably the man most responsible for
making rock'n'roll successful in the first place, was about to stand trial, accused of
accepting bribes (payola) for playing certain rock records on the radio. Rock music
had lost its cutting edge since Freed's heyday, but unbeknown to him and to most of
the world, that early excitement was about to be rekindled by The Beatles and their
contemporaries – the latest in a long line of great British HIT PARADE HEROES.

Index

British Beat Before The Beatles is a 7 CD 140 track selection of the best of British Beat from 1955-1962. It traces the effect of American rock 'n' roll on British musicians and the rise of the first of the UK's pop stars such as Marty Wilde, Tommy Steele, Billy Fury and Cliff Richard. *The series is released between July And October 1993.*

VOLUME ONE - (1955 -1956)
CATALOGUE NO: CDGO 2046 (CDP 7892202)

1. Tweedle Dee - Susie Miller
2. Earth Angel - The Southlanders
3. Dance With Me Henry - Susie Miller
4. (We're Gonna) Rock Around The Clock - Deep River Boys
5. Ain't that A Shame - The Southlanders
6. Rock Island Line - Lonnie Donegan
7. My Boy Flat Top - Frankie Vaughan
8. Dungaree Doll - Dickie Bennett
9. Tutti Frutti - Four Jones Boys
10. Why Do Fools Fall In Love - Alma Cogan
11. Bad Penny Blues - Humphrey Lyttlelton
12. Rock 'n' Roll Blues - Don Lang
13. Left Hand Boogie - Ray Ellington
14. I'm In Love Again - Alma Cogan
15. Teach You To Rock - Tony Crombie & His Rockets
16. Rock With the Caveman - Tommy Steele
17. Giddy Up A Ding-Dong - Ray Ellington
18. Don't Nobody Move - Lee Lawrence
19. Let's You And I Rock - Tony Crombie & His Rockets
20. Singing The Blues - Tommy Steele

British Beat Before The Beatles
Volume One • 1955-1956   mono
A HISTORY OF BRITISH BEAT BEFORE THE BEATLES
Greatest Artists · Finest Recording

VOLUME 2 (1957)
CATALOGUE NO: CDGO 2047 (CDP 7892212)

1. Don't Knock The Rock - Art Baxter & His Rock 'n' Roll Sinners
2. A White Sport Coat (And A Pink Carnation) - King Brothers
3. Don't You Rock Me Daddy-O - The Vipers Skiffle Group
4. Party Doll - Ricky James
5. School Day (Ring Ring Goes The Bell) - Don Lang & His Frantic Five
6. Bye Bye Love - Rory Blackwell
7. Start Movin' - Larry Page
8. Fabulous - Alma Cogan
9. Butterfly - Tommy Steele
10. Matchbox - Terry Wayne
11. Wanderin' Eyes - Frankie Vaughan
12. Be My Girl - Jim Dale
13. Your True Love - Terry Wayne
14. That'll Be The Day - Larry Page
15. He's Got The Whole World In His Hands - Laurie London
16. Red Planet Rock - Don Lang & His Frantic Five
17. Trying To Get To You - Joey Castell
18. Baby She's Gone - Terry Dene
19. Empty Arms Blues - Colin Hicks & The Cabin Boys
20. I'm Left, You're Right, She's Gone - Joey Castell

VOLUME 3 (1958)
CATALOGUE NO: CDGO 2048 (CDP 7892222)

1. Slim Jim Tie - Terry Wayne
2. Raunchy - Ken Mackintosh
3. Under Control - Larry Page
4. Riot In Cell Black No. 9 - Wee Willie Harris
5. Whole Lotta Woman - Most Brothers
6. Yea Yea - Vince Eager And The Vagabonds
7. Book Of Love - The Mudlarks (with the Ken Jones Jive Group)

8. Endless Sleep - Marty Wilde and His Wildcats
9. Mercy, Mercy, Mercy - Neville Taylor
10. Teenage Love - The Five Chesternuts
11. Nothin' Shakin' - Craig Douglas
12. Move It - Cliff Richard And The Drifters
13. Hoots Moon - Lord Rockingham's Xl
14. Come On Let's Go - Tommy Steele
15. Tears On My Pillow - Neville Taylor And The Cutters
16. Pretty Little Pearly - Terrry Dene
17. No More - Vince Eager
18. This Little Girl's Gone Rockin' - Janice Peters with the Frank Barber Band
19. Queen Of The Hop - Don Lang
20. High School Confidential - Adam Faith

VOLUME 4 - (1959)
CATALOGUE NO: CDGO 2049 (CDP 7892232)

1. Maybe Tomorrow - Billy Fury
2. Brand New Cadillac - Vince Taylor And His Playboys
3. Once More - Bill Forbes
4. A Girl Likes - Janice Peters
5. Slippin' 'n' Slidin' - Dickie Pride
6. Hey Miss Fannie - Dean Webb
7. This Should Go On Forever - Vince Eager
8. Please Don't Touch - Johnny Kidd And The Pirates
9. Teenager In Love - Marty Wilde
10. Dream Lover - Duffy Power
11. Ah Poor Little Baby - Adam Faith
12. She's Mine - Terry Wayne
13. Apron Strings - Cliff Richard and The Drifters
14. Only Sixteen - Craig Douglas
15. Tallahassie Lassie - Tommy Steele
16. Jet Black - The Drifters
17. Frantic - Dickie Pride
18. I Don't Know- Lorne Lesley
19. Little Cutie - Sally Kelly
20. What Do you Want To Make Those Eyes At Me For? - Emile Ford and The Checkmates

British Beat Before The Beatles
Volume Two • 1957   mono
A HISTORY OF BRITISH BEAT BEFORE THE BEATLES

VOLUME 5 (1960)
CATALOGUE NO: CDGO 2050 (CDP 7892242)

1. Saturday Dance - The Shadows
2. Betty Betty (Goin' Steady With Me) - Dickie Pride
3. Lonely Boy Blue - Vince Eager
4. Amapola - Davy Jones
5. If You Don't Know - Jody Gibson And The Muleskinners
6. (Must You Always) Tease Me - Keith Kelly
7. Sweet Dreams - Dave Sampson & The Hunters
8. Sixteen Reason - Marion Ryan
9. Ain't Misbehavin' - Tommy Bruce & The Bruisers
10. You'll Never know What You Miss - Emile Ford And The Checkmates
11. That's Love - Billy Fury
12. Shakin' All Over - Johnny Kidd And The Pirates
13. Made You (From the film *Beat Girl*) - Adam Faith

14. Apache - Bert Weedon
15. Angry - Marty Wilde
16. Tell Laura I Love Her - Ricky Valance
17. Walk Don't Run - The John Barry Seven
18. Nine Times Out Of Ten - Cliff Richard And The Shadows
19. Restless - Johnny Kidd & The Pirates
20. Teen Scene - The Hunters

British Beat Before The Beatles
Volume Three • 1958   mono
A HISTORY OF No.3 BRITISH BEAT BEFORE THE BEATLES 1958 1958

VOLUME 6 (1961)
CATALOGUE NO: CDGO 2051 (CDP 7892252)

1. Music - Robb Storme And The Whispers
2. Teenage Love - Michael Cox
3. High Class Feeling - Josh MacRae
4. Are You Sure - The Allisons
5. Don't Treat Me Like A Child - Helen Shapiro
6. Gee Wizz It's You - Cliff Richard
7. Halfway To Paradise - Billy Fury
8. Trambone - The Krew Kats
9. I'll Step Down - Lee Diamond And The Cherokees
10. You've Got What I Like - Cliff Bennett And The Rebel Rousers
11. Sweet Little Sixteen - Michael Cox
12. Baby Sittin' - Bobby Angelo And The Tuxedos
13. All Grown Up - Paul Raven
14. I'm A Moody Guy - Shane Fenton And The Fentones
15. Please Don't Bring Me Down - Johnny Kidd And The Pirates
16. When I Get Paid - Cliff Bennett
17. Tomorrow's Clown - Marty Wilde
18. The Savage - The Shadows
19. 'Til The Following Night - Screaming Lord Sutch With The Savages
20. Your Ma Said You Cried In Your Sleep Last Night - Doug Sheldon

VOLUME 7 (1962)
CATALOGUE NO: CDGO 2052 (CDP 7892262)

1. Someone To Love - Brad Newman
2. True Fine Mama - Howie Casey And The Seniors
3. Lessons In Love - The Allisons
4. Honey 'cause I Love You - Michael Cox
5. Wonderful Land - The Shadows
6. Sugar Babe (Part 1) - Jimmy Powell
7. The Mexican - The Fentones
8. A Picture Of You - Joe Brown And The Bruvvers
9. I Sold My Heart To The Junkman - Lyn Cornell
10. I Shoulda Listened To Mama - Jimmy Crawford
11. Johnny Get Angry - Carol Deene
12. It'll Be Me - Cliff Richard And The Shadows
13. Why Little Girl - Shane Fentone And The Fentones
14. Stand Up - Michael Cox
15. Ever Since You Said Goodbye - Marty Wilde
16. All Of Me - Jackie Lynton
17. Dance On - The Shadows
18. Ubangi Stomp - Dean Shannon
19. I Can Tell - Johnny Kidd And The Pirates
20. A Shot Of Rhythm And Blues - Johnny Kidd And The Pirates